To the
Ends of the
Universe

To the
Ends of the
Universe

A voyage through life, space and time

Heather Couper and Nigel Henbest

Illustrated by Luciano Corbella

DORLING KINDERSLEY

LONDON • NEW YORK • MOSCOW • SYDNEY

A DORLING KINDERSLEY BOOK

First published in 1998
by Dorling Kindersley Limited
9 Henrietta Street, London WC2E 8PS

2 4 6 8 10 9 7 5 3 1

A CIP catalogue record for this book is available from the British Library

ISBN 0-7513-5825-8

Reproduced by Colourscan, Singapore
Printed in Italy by L.E.G.O.

Contents

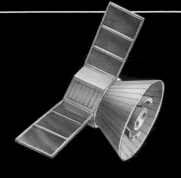

Introduction

"HERE BE DRAGONS..." These words, engraved on world maps over the depths of the African jungle or the far realms of the Asian desert, speak of the spell that *terra incognita* cast over medieval cartographers. Today, we may have eradicated the monsters – and most of the mysteries – from our world. But the heavens above constitute a new frontier, where we can still encounter the unexpected, the unusual, and the astounding.

Black holes, the Big Bang, the birth of planets like Earth, the existence of aliens... these are the monsters and mysteries of today's explorers, the astronomers and scientists set on the quest of understanding not just one small planet, but a whole Universe.

The Quest for Knowledge

Venture out under the immense panorama of the night sky, and even today we feel an overwhelming sense of awe; faced with infinity we are humbled.

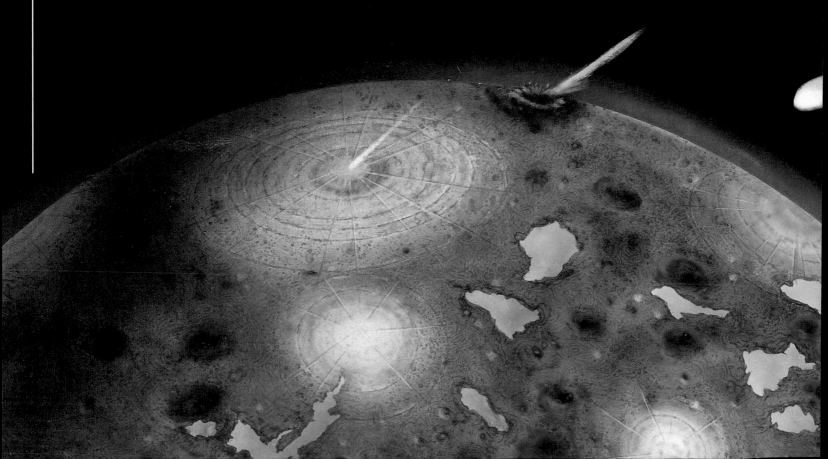

However, scientists now claim to understand the cosmos. And, although they cannot yet control its might, their knowledge has undoubtedly conferred power. Astronomers can peer into Nature's ultimate abyss, the black hole; they can begin to predict what our cosmic neighbours may be like; and they have begun to unlock the secrets of creation itself.

This is is not merely *fin-de-millennial* bragging. The answers to the Big Questions of the Universe are now within our grasp – built on firm foundations with centuries of questioning and deep scientific research.

First Impressions

The quest begins in the remote recesses of the prehistoric world – astronomers have been heard to boast that they are members of the second oldest profession! The alignment of the mighty megaliths of Stonehenge with the midsummer sunrise, and the four-square setting of the Pyramids with the cardinal compass points both indicate the deep roots of human preoccupation with the sky.

From the beginning, the greatest minds must have pondered the nature of the firmament above and beyond our world of earth, water, and air. First impressions on the human psyche seem to be of a heaven very different from the mundane world. Around the globe we find creation myths where the sky is sundered from the Earth, each the realm of a contrasting primeval deity. In Egypt, the sky goddess Nut was forced to arch her body upwards, on her toes and fingertips, above the recumbent body of her brother and one-time lover the earth god Geb.

Bedazzled by the myriad stars in their dark skies, the early Greeks believed the night literally had a thousand eyes – sewn onto the mantle of the celestial night watchman Argos. But around the Aegean the stage was set for a more subtle interpretation. A new breed of philosopher – the earliest on record is Thales of Miletus – took a giant leap for mankind's intellect. Suppose, they mused, that the heavens were not intrinsically different from the Earth.

In the 4th century BC, Eudoxus of Cnidus suggested that the planets were not circling the sky under the control of wilful gods, but instead were carried on rotating spheres of crystal. The "mysteries" of the cosmos were not accessible solely by divine revelation; they could be solved by rational human thought.

In Renaissance Italy, Galileo Galilei blew sky-high the old crystal spheres: the stars, he claimed, were other suns, dimmed by their enormous distance from us. His compatriot, Giordano Bruno, went so far as to state that each was accompanied by some kind of alien life – and was burnt at the stake for his belief. William Herschel, in 18th-century England, proposed that all worlds must be inhabited including the Moon, Saturn, and even the fiery Sun!

The Search Continues

Science has not been kind to such a plurality of inhabited worlds. Except for possible bacteria – now fossilized – on Mars and speculative swimming creatures beneath the icy crust of Jupiter's moon Europa, there is little hope of other life in the Solar System. But astronomers have now proved Bruno's conviction of planets circling other stars – more planets are known outside the Solar System than are circling the Sun. Biologists have teamed with astronomers to provide answers that are more than guesswork to the question of how life might have evolved elsewhere. And the search is on for radio signals from other civilizations "out there"...

Another forecast from Herschel's time has already met with success – a prediction even more outlandish than alien life. A Yorkshire clergyman, John Michell, took Isaac Newton's theory of gravity to its logical conclusion.

It was possible, he maintained, to find "stars" where gravity was so powerful that nothing – not even light – could escape. Two hundred years on, astronomers have discovered these irresistible and invisible traps, the ultimate monsters of the Universe. Today we call them black holes.

The Ultimate Journey

And, in the past few decades, astronomers have solved the biggest mystery of all. How did everything begin? Until this century, the question – let alone the answer – was the prerogative of theologians and philosophers. Scientists trod as warily on this territory as they did in discussing the nature of the human soul.

Yet now the answer is known. All the matter in the Universe – along with space and time – was formed in a colossal explosion, the Big Bang. The evidence piles in year by year: galaxies are racing apart, like shrapnel from a grenade; matter around us bears the signs of being cooked in a billion-degree furnace; the Universe is filled with a warm "afterglow" of the original fireball... Some details have yet to be ironed out, including the date of creation, but the fact that the Big Bang happened is as certain as the existence of atoms as the basis of matter, or DNA as the library of inheritance.

At the close of the second millennium and the dawn of the third, we come to one of the great defining points of humanity. The meaning of life; the ultimate devastation of the black hole; the crucible of creation; we can now make the ultimate journeys to these lands of the cosmic dragon, and know what lies at our destination at the ends of the Universe.

Big Bang

HOW DID THE UNIVERSE BEGIN?

Once the ultimate mystery, all the evidence now points to the birth of our Universe in circumstances of unimaginable power and fury. We call it the Big Bang: an event that not only created the Universe, but also the whole of space and time.

This section of the book takes you on a vivid journey of discovery through the life story of the cosmos. It follows the Universe from its infancy and turbulent youth to the present, and into its old age – trillions and trillions of years in the future. It also explores many of the questions that arise from contemplating the Universe on its grandest scales. What was there before the Big Bang? What made the Big Bang happen? How old is the Universe? How big is it? Could there be other universes?

Big Bang examines the very latest findings in cosmology – a subject right at the cutting edge of astronomical science. It explains why the infant fireball created the matter that surrounds us today, and how the four forces of nature came into being. It investigates the weird particles that populated the young cosmos, looks at the latest evidence that proves that the Big Bang really happened, and probes the echoes of the Big Bang that resonate around us even now.

Cosmologists today can even look to the future of the Universe. Will our currently expanding Universe continue to expand forever, becoming an ever-growing emptiness? Or will it one day reach a limit and then start to collapse, eventually re-coalescing into an ultra-dense state? And might another Big Bang arise from this "Big Crunch" – creating a completely different Universe?

Countdown

IN THE BEGINNING, THERE WAS NOTHING. It was a "nothing" so profound it defies human comprehension. We may think of the emptiest parts of the Universe today — out in the cold realms between the distant galaxies — as "nothing regions". But even they contain a sprinkling of atoms, and the faint radiation of dim shafts of light passing through. More fundamentally, the emptiest regions today are supported by the invisible structure of space, and respond to the inaudible clock of time. A long, long time ago, there was no matter, and no radiation. More importantly, space did not exist; time did not flow. Our story begins "once upon a time" — when there was no space, and there was no time.

No time

Time is not an ever-rolling stream, flowing from forever in the past to forever in the future. The flow of time is intimately linked into space — and into matter and gravity. We cannot speak of what happened before the Big Bang, because time itself did not exist then.

No space

Before space was created, nothing could exist; there was nowhere for it to exist in. Our Universe probably came into existence not only from nothing, but from nowhere.

Why?

Science cannot answer the question why the Universe began. Why didn't the original "nothing" stay that way? Philosophers and theologians have their own answers, which can probably never be proven one way or the other. All we do know is that something did happen.

T equals zero

FROM NOTHING, a tiny speck of brilliant light appeared. It was almost infinitely hot. Inside this fireball was all of space. With the creation of space came the birth of time: the great cosmic clock began to tick, some 13 billion years ago. The energy in the fireball was so concentrated that matter spontaneously started to appear: a distant ancestor of the matter that would later become the building blocks of stars, planets, and galaxies. The infant Universe hit the ground running. As soon as the fireball appeared, it started expanding – not into anything, but throughout, because the Universe was, and is, everything and everywhere. In the first trillion-trillion-trillionth of a second, shown here, the Universe grew a hundred million times bigger, while its temperature dropped from near infinity to 10,000 trillion trillion degrees.

DAWN OF TIME
There was no "before" the Big Bang, because time did not exist. When there was no space and no matter, there was no such thing as time, either. Cosmologists believe space and time are intimately linked. Once time existed, space could start to expand; once space was created, time was able to flow.

The Big Bang took place about 13 billion years ago.

ORIGINS OF SPACE
The Big Bang was not an explosion *into* anything – it happened everywhere: there was no surrounding empty space. Space itself was created at the instant of the Big Bang. Astronomers see the aftermath of creation all around us today, in the continued expansion of the Universe. The galaxies – "star cities" – appear to be rushing away from each other at high speeds. But in reality, it is the space between the galaxies that is stretching, carrying them apart.

A small fragment of the Universe begins to expand.

The growing Universe starts to cool, changing colour and growing dimmer.

In reality, the temperature of the infant Universe is so high that it always appears blindingly bright during this period.

RECREATING THE BIG BANG
When scientists investigate the origin of the Universe, their tools are not telescopes, but particle accelerators. The closest they can come to the very early Universe is to recreate its searingly diabolic conditions in high-energy accelerators, where powerful electric fields accelerate particles such as electrons until they are travelling very close to the velocity of light, nature's ultimate speed limit. When these particles smash head-on in a paroxysm of energy, an exotic array of subatomic particles fleetingly appears, only to disappear fractions of a second later. Such particles were commonly found in the early days of the Big Bang.

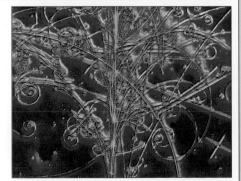

The Big Bang revisited: these are tracks from particles, created in an accelerator, that are rarely found in today's Universe.

As space expands, the density rapidly falls. It starts at an incredible 10 billion trillion trillion trillion trillion trillion trillion grams per cubic centimetre.

Even the most sophisticated theories cannot tell us what happened at the exact instant of creation. The earliest we can wind the clock back to is 10 million-trillion-trillion-trillionths of a second after creation.

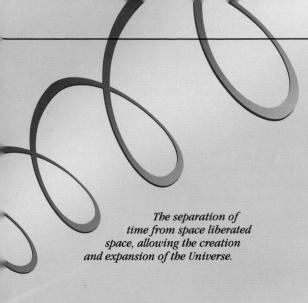

The separation of time from space liberated space, allowing the creation and expansion of the Universe.

The raging inferno

The infant Universe was searingly hot, brimming with the energy of intense radiation. Albert Einstein's famous equation $E=mc^2$ says that mass and energy are interchangeable: one can be turned into the other. In the early Universe, the energy of the radiation was so intense that it could spontaneously turn into "lumps" of matter. These took the form of subatomic particles, such as electrons, and their antimatter partners, such as positrons. Antimatter has exactly the opposite properties to matter and, if the two meet, they destroy, or annihilate, each other. The particles and antiparticles lasted just fractions of a second before mutually annihilating in a burst of energy that converted them back to radiation – which then created more matter-antimatter pairs.

A SMALL MATTER OF CREATION

The phrase "Big Bang" is not a very accurate one. The Universe actually started with a rather small – not to say puny – bang. Even the amount of energy involved in the expansion was rather paltry. If converted into matter, it would amount to only about 1 kg (2 lb), or the equivalent of a bag of sugar.

The fledgling Universe does not contain matter as we know it, or familiar forces like gravity. Instead, matter, radiation, and forces are tangled together in a totally unfamiliar scrum.

MICROSCOPIC CAULDRON

If you could take a microscope to the early Universe, it would appear as a seething cauldron of radiation and subatomic particles forever appearing and disappearing.

Particles can literally materialize from a momentary concentration of energy. The result is a pair of subatomic particles, one made of matter, the other antimatter.

The particles and antiparticles try to fly apart, but in the dense fireball they quickly meet up again.

As they collide, the particles and antiparticles annihilate each other in a flash of radiation. This energy returns to the seething pool of radiation in the fireball, in a continuing cycle of creation and annihilation.

GHOSTLY PARTICLES

Even in a vacuum, matter and antimatter can spontaneously appear. A pair of particles and antiparticles can materialize by "borrowing" energy from the vacuum. They are known as virtual particles because they must annihilate themselves almost immediately and return the energy debt.

SMALL AND LIFELESS

If the Universe had continued to expand like this, it would have ended up small, sparse – and lifeless. But something amazing happened…

Blow-up

SUDDENLY, THE UNIVERSE BLEW UP! In practically no time at all, it grew a hundred trillion trillion trillion trillion times. And its once searing temperature dropped to almost zero. This phenomenal growth is called "cosmic inflation". In comparison, the original Big Bang was about as spectacular as a hand grenade going off in a nuclear war. As quickly as it had started, inflation came to an end. Now the temperature shot up again and particles of matter and antimatter appeared. Inflation solves many problems that the straightforward Big Bang theory cannot answer. It explains why the Universe is so big and smooth, why different forces act in it today, and where the vast amount of matter came from.

INVENTOR OF INFLATION

In 1979, Alan Guth was a particle physicist at the Stanford Linear Accelerator Center in California interested in how the forces might be unified – the "Grand Unified Theory". His calculations led to the idea of cosmic inflation. Since then, Guth's theory of inflation has answered more questions about the Universe than he originally sought to answer.

Alan Guth was only 32 when he devised his theory of inflation.

Cosmic inflation

The young Universe contained more energy than it knew what to do with, and it entered a period of instability. One effect of this was to fuel a dramatic growth spurt. Between ten trillion-trillion-trillionths of a second and ten billion-trillion-trillionths of a second (usually written 10^{-35} and 10^{-32} seconds – see Glossary) after the Big Bang, the Universe underwent a dramatic period of inflation. The end result was not only a Universe 100 trillion trillion trillion trillion times bigger, but the creation of the vast amounts of matter that fill the Universe today.

An instant after creation, the Universe is almost infinitely hot and expanding quite slowly.

This portion shown here contains only enough energy to make 1 kg (2 lb) of matter and measures 10^{-23} cm across, far smaller than an atom.

Had inflation not happened, the Universe might have collapsed back on itself and self-destructed – after existing for less than a second.

The young Universe cools as it expands.

Pre-inflation, the Universe has a temperature of 10^{28} degrees or 10,000 trillion trillion degrees.

As the temperature drops to below 10^{28} degrees, the Universe suddenly inflates. It doubles its size every 10^{-34} seconds, rapidly cooling as it does so.

Why the Universe we live in is so smooth

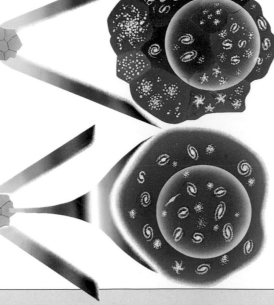

If inflation had not happened, the Universe we see today (within the sphere) would be like a patchwork quilt of different regions. Instead, the Universe is very uniform.

Inflation had the effect of expanding each region of the early Universe so that it became immense. We are well inside one region, so our neighbourhood appears uniform.

Today, the Universe is incredibly smooth: wherever astronomers look in the Universe, they see the same kinds of galaxies and measure the same background temperature. This is a problem for cosmologists, who predict that different portions of space in the Big Bang would have had slightly differing temperatures and densities. These would have grown into a patchwork of diverse regions in the Universe around us. The theory of inflation offers a way out. Each original portion from the Big Bang has grown immensely larger than the Universe we can see, so our observable Universe lies entirely within just one of these regions.

The few existing particles and antiparticles are scattered far and wide, so the enormously expanded Universe is an almost perfect vacuum.

Although the Universe is effectively a vacuum it is packed with pairs of virtual particles, which are continually appearing and disappearing.

By the end of inflation – 10^{-32} seconds after the Big Bang – the temperature has fallen to almost absolute zero (0 Kelvin or –273 °C).

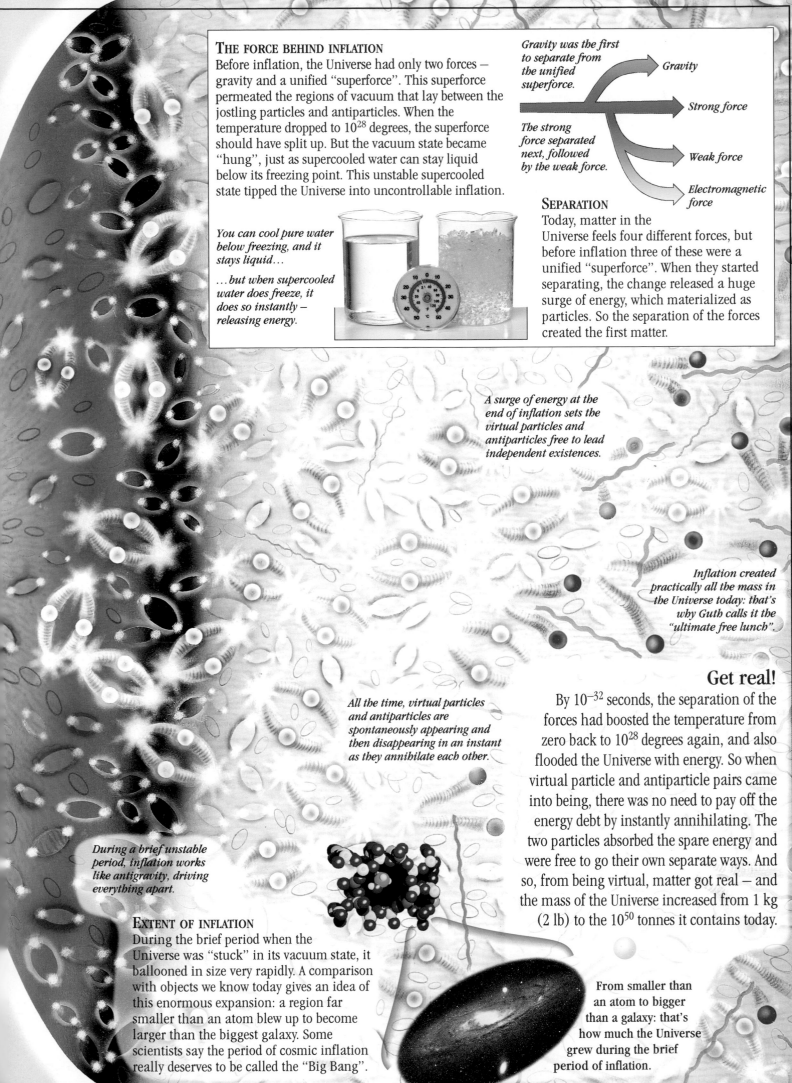

THE FORCE BEHIND INFLATION

Before inflation, the Universe had only two forces — gravity and a unified "superforce". This superforce permeated the regions of vacuum that lay between the jostling particles and antiparticles. When the temperature dropped to 10^{28} degrees, the superforce should have split up. But the vacuum state became "hung", just as supercooled water can stay liquid below its freezing point. This unstable supercooled state tipped the Universe into uncontrollable inflation.

You can cool pure water below freezing, and it stays liquid…

…but when supercooled water does freeze, it does so instantly — releasing energy.

Gravity was the first to separate from the unified superforce.

Gravity

Strong force

The strong force separated next, followed by the weak force.

Weak force

Electromagnetic force

SEPARATION

Today, matter in the Universe feels four different forces, but before inflation three of these were a unified "superforce". When they started separating, the change released a huge surge of energy, which materialized as particles. So the separation of the forces created the first matter.

A surge of energy at the end of inflation sets the virtual particles and antiparticles free to lead independent existences.

Inflation created practically all the mass in the Universe today: that's why Guth calls it the "ultimate free lunch".

All the time, virtual particles and antiparticles are spontaneously appearing and then disappearing in an instant as they annihilate each other.

Get real!

By 10^{-32} seconds, the separation of the forces had boosted the temperature from zero back to 10^{28} degrees again, and also flooded the Universe with energy. So when virtual particle and antiparticle pairs came into being, there was no need to pay off the energy debt by instantly annihilating. The two particles absorbed the spare energy and were free to go their own separate ways. And so, from being virtual, matter got real — and the mass of the Universe increased from 1 kg (2 lb) to the 10^{50} tonnes it contains today.

During a brief unstable period, inflation works like antigravity, driving everything apart.

EXTENT OF INFLATION

During the brief period when the Universe was "stuck" in its vacuum state, it ballooned in size very rapidly. A comparison with objects we know today gives an idea of this enormous expansion: a region far smaller than an atom blew up to become larger than the biggest galaxy. Some scientists say the period of cosmic inflation really deserves to be called the "Big Bang".

From smaller than an atom to bigger than a galaxy: that's how much the Universe grew during the brief period of inflation.

Particle soup

Hot on the heels of its dramatic inflation, the Universe embarked on the most frenetic period in its entire history. Fuelled by the tremendous surge of energy released, it launched itself into an orgy of matter creation. Many of the particles forged in that inferno no longer exist. In this early phase, when it was all of ten billion-trillion-trillionths of a second old, the Universe experimented with exotic creations that rapidly decayed, or changed into other particles. This era was one of total turmoil. The scene must have looked like a view through an out-of-control kaleidoscope, or a speeded-up movie of fish swarming round a coral reef.

Magnetic monopole: *Heavy particle with only one magnetic pole (ordinary magnets have two) predicted by the Grand Unified Theory. It is thought to determine the electric charge of other particles, such as quarks and electrons.*

Leptons: *Lightweight particles such as electrons that are sensitive to the weak force.*

Snapshot of a subatomic world

An enormously magnified snapshot of the Universe would reveal an intensely hot "soup" of seething subatomic particles and antiparticles (shown as solid and semi-solid spheres, respectively). Some are still around today, while others have disappeared. Quarks, leptons, WIMPs, cosmic strings, and primordial black holes cannoned around like tiny billiard balls. Gluons, W and Z bosons, and gravitons – which are found today mainly as "messengers" carrying the forces – then existed as real particles.

WIMPs: *Weakly interacting massive particles, which may comprise most of the dark matter believed to make up 90 per cent of the mass of the present-day Universe.*

Quark: *Today, these are the building blocks of protons and neutrons in the nuclei of atoms. There are six known varieties or "flavours".*

W or Z boson

The weak force, governed by W and Z bosons, controls the energy of the Sun.

THE FOUR FORCES

The four fundamental forces we know today have vastly different strengths, and affect different particles. Gravity, by far the weakest, influences all particles, while the most powerful, the strong force, works only inside the nucleus of atoms. At high energies, the strong force weakens, while the electromagnetic and weak forces grow stronger. Physicists believe they were once all one force (but separate from gravity). This is the Grand Unified Theory, which predicts the existence of X bosons and cosmic strings.

Gluon

The strong force, carried by gluons, makes an atom bomb explode.

W and Z bosons: *Particles, similar to the photon but with mass, that convey the weak force.*

Graviton: *The particle thought to convey gravitational force, although it has not yet been detected.*

Photon

Photons, conveyed by the electromagnetic force, drive communications.

Graviton

Gravity, thought to be conveyed by gravitons, pulls free-fall parachutists to Earth.

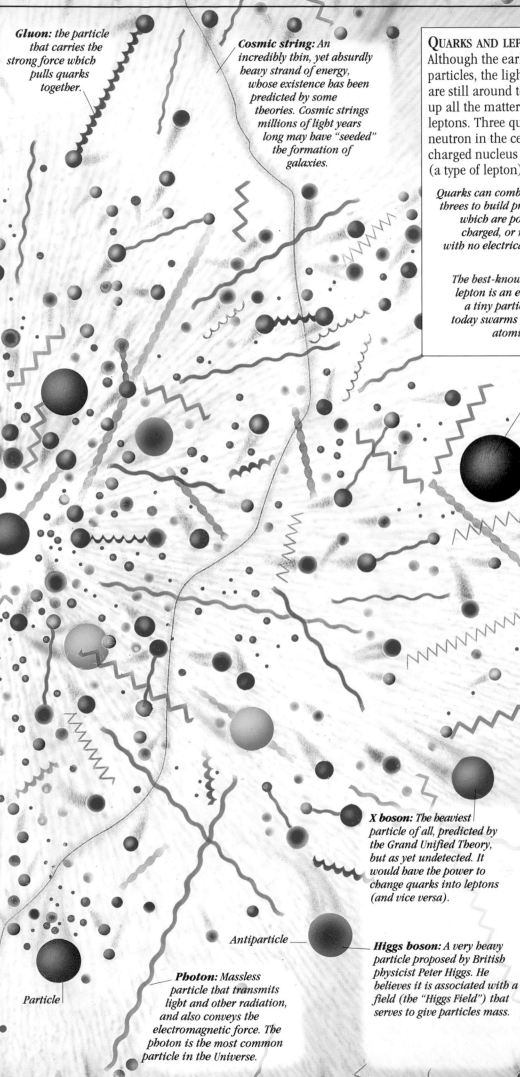

Gluon: *the particle that carries the strong force which pulls quarks together.*

Cosmic string: *An incredibly thin, yet absurdly heavy strand of energy, whose existence has been predicted by some theories. Cosmic strings millions of light years long may have "seeded" the formation of galaxies.*

QUARKS AND LEPTONS: THE SURVIVORS

Although the early Universe contained many massive particles, the lightweight particles were the survivors, and are still around today. Atoms — the basic units that make up all the matter around us — are built up of quarks and leptons. Three quarks apiece make up each proton and neutron in the central nucleus of an atom. The positively charged nucleus is balanced by the negative electrons (a type of lepton) swarming around it.

Quarks can combine in threes to build protons, which are positively charged, or neutrons, with no electrical charge.

An antiquark, made of anti-matter, has the opposite properties to a quark. If the two meet, they annihilate each other.

The best-known type of lepton is an electron, a tiny particle that today swarms around atomic nuclei.

Antileptons are the antimatter equivalent of leptons. The electron's opposite number is a positron.

Primordial black hole: *A mini black hole, the size of an atom but as heavy as a mountain. The British physicist Stephen Hawking believes that many were created in the early Universe, but none has yet been found.*

Neutrino: *The second most common particle in the Universe. Neutrinos are leptons, and come in three varieties. They are so lightweight that their mass has yet to be measured. If they had even a small mass, neutrinos could make up the dark matter in the Universe.*

NEUTRINO ASTRONOMY

Every second, a hundred billion neutrinos from the Big Bang pass through your body. They have survived unchanged from the era of "particle soup": by studying them, scientists could check their theories of the earliest moments of the Universe. Unfortunately, neutrinos are difficult to catch. Physicists have detected some from the Sun and a supernova, but none so far from the Big Bang.

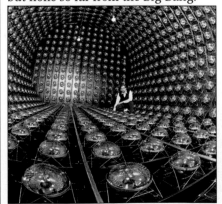

Inside a "neutrino telescope" in New Mexico, USA.

X boson: *The heaviest particle of all, predicted by the Grand Unified Theory, but as yet undetected. It would have the power to change quarks into leptons (and vice versa).*

Antiparticle

Higgs boson: *A very heavy particle proposed by British physicist Peter Higgs. He believes it is associated with a field (the "Higgs Field") that serves to give particles mass.*

Photon: *Massless particle that transmits light and other radiation, and also conveys the electromagnetic force. The photon is the most common particle in the Universe.*

Particle

Creation of matter

THE UNIVERSE BECAME A BATTLEGROUND as it entered its next phase. Thronged with subatomic particles of all kinds fighting for supremacy, there was also constant warfare between equally matched battalions of matter and antimatter. A particle and its antiparticle counterpart would inevitably meet up and destroy one another. The radiation produced in these skirmishes helped fuel the action, providing the energy to create still more particle-antiparticle pairs. But by the time the Universe was a second old, all was quiet: antimatter had been vanquished and matter ruled.

COOLING CONDITIONS

The Universe changed dramatically between 10^{-32} and 1 second. As the relentless expansion continued, the Universe cooled. In the hot, early stages, massive particles and antiparticles were common. By the end of the era, when temperatures had dropped to 10 billion degrees, most of the massive particles had gone, antimatter had all but disappeared, and quarks were ganging up to make the matter we know today.

The X boson and its counterpart, the anti-X, soon disappear. The temperature rapidly drops too low to create particles this heavy. The existing X bosons and anti-Xs are unstable, and decay into showers of leptons, quarks, and their antiparticles.

PERIOD OF CHANGE

Throughout this period, the Universe was a turmoil of annihilation, decay, and the creation of new matter-antimatter pairs. Here we highlight just a few of the most important milestones.

W and Z bosons decay into lighter particles. From now on, they appear only as messenger particles that convey the weak force between quarks and leptons. Scientists first recreated W and Z bosons at the CERN particle accelerator laboratory in Switzerland in 1983.

The richness of the original exotic particle soup quickly turned into a thin gruel of more homely particles as the Universe expanded and cooled.

A BIAS TOWARDS MATTER

The power of inflation created exactly equal amounts of matter and antimatter. So why did they not wipe each other out? The answer may lie with the massive X boson and its counterpart, the anti-X. As the Universe cooled, the X and anti-X both decayed into lighter particles and antiparticles (quarks and leptons). But both kinds of decay slightly favoured matter: for every 100,000,000 quarks and leptons created, there were only 99,999,999 antiquarks and antileptons. This tiny imbalance has resulted in the stars, planets, and galaxies that populate our Universe today.

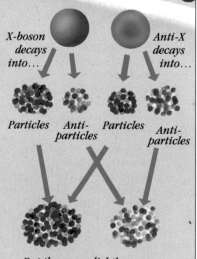

X-boson decays into…   *Anti-X decays into…*

Particles   *Anti-particles*   *Particles*   *Anti-particles*

But there are slightly more particles than antiparticles.

SEARCHING FOR ANTIMATTER

How do we know that some objects in the Universe are *not* made of antimatter? The answer is that every part of space is in contact with its neighbouring region. If a region of antimatter existed, astronomers would detect flashes of radiation at its boundary, where the anti-atoms met up with ordinary atoms in the adjacent region. Astronomers have looked for such tell-tale radiation, without success.

An Andromeda Galaxy made of antimatter would look the same as one made of matter. The same goes for humans – but beware of shaking hands with your antimatter counterpart!

Annihilation and decay

Particles were constantly disappearing: they either annihilated on meeting their antiparticles or they decayed into lighter particles. Meanwhile, particle-antiparticle pairs were being regenerated from the intense radiation all around. But as the Universe cooled, it could no longer make the heaviest particle-antiparticle pairs, and they became extinct.

A millionth of a second after the Big Bang, the temperature drops so low that the radiation can no longer create quark-antiquark pairs. The remaining antiquarks annihilate with the more numerous quarks, leaving a small residue of quarks.

A FAMILY OF QUARKS

The quark family got its name from a quote in James Joyce's book *Finnegans Wake*: "Three quarks for Mr Mark". There are six quarks (three pairs): from heaviest to lightest they are top and bottom, charm and strange, and up and down. All quarks carry an electric charge: some are positive (such as the up quark) and some negative (such as the down quark). Only the two lightest quarks are stable – the others decay into down and up quarks.

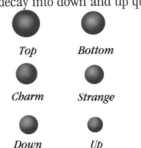

Top
Bottom
Charm
Strange
Down
Up

Today, quarks live in twos or threes. This up-down-up arrangement is a positively charged proton.

The slightly heavier down-up-down arrangement is a neutron. The quarks are held together by gluons.

The lightest antiparticles, the antileptons, survive longer than any other kind of antimatter. The remaining antileptons annihilated with the more numerous leptons, leaving a small residue of leptons.

The first multiple particles, made of three quarks joined together by gluons, come together one ten-thousandth of a second after the Big Bang. These composite particles are protons and neutrons, which will form the nuclei of today's atoms.

Although the neutrinos and WIMPs will never make up atoms, planets, or stars, they will become crucial players in the Universe. WIMPs or neutrinos – or both – may form the dark matter whose gravity controls the motion of galaxies and dictates the ultimate fate of the Universe.

LIGHTEST LASTS LONGEST

Leptons are lightweight particles (lepton is taken from the Greek word for "light"). There are six types of leptons: the tau, the muon, and the electron, and their associated neutrinos. Leptons can have an electric charge (for example, the electron), or none at all. Tau and muon leptons are unstable, and eventually decay into electrons and neutrinos. All three types of neutrinos are stable.

Tau
Tau neutrino
Muon
Muon neutrino
Electron
Electron neutrino

The survivors

The building blocks of matter today – protons, neutrons, and electrons – were a minor constituent of the Universe at the age of one second. All around, in vast numbers, were neutrinos. Surviving among these lightweight particles, there may have been massive remnants of the past: WIMPS, magnetic monopoles, cosmic strings, and primordial black holes. But above all, there was light. Photons (particles of light and other radiation, such as gamma rays) outnumbered matter particles by 100 million to one.

First elements

COMPARED WITH AN INSTANT before, the one-second-old Universe was a model of restraint. Nevertheless, it seethed with activity — busier than it would be at any period in the next few hundred thousand years. Packed with dazzling photons, neutrinos, and WIMPs, rushing around in temperatures of 10 billion degrees, there was also a minuscule number of protons, neutrons, and electrons. Over the next three minutes, the expanding cosmos cooled into a place where construction could begin. By the end of the third minute, the basic building blocks — the protons and neutrons — had created the kind of matter we would recognize today, the first three elements.

Cosmic oven

The young Universe had a head start in creating elements, because some of its protons would become the nuclei of the simplest element, hydrogen. But it had only the briefest of times to build anything more complex. Before the first second, conditions were just too energetic: intense radiation zapped apart fragile partnerships between protons and neutrons. And after three minutes, the relentless expansion of the Universe drove would-be coalitions of particles apart. Between these extremes, the environment was just right for cooking up the nuclei of the elements helium and lithium.

Proton

Neutron

1 HEAVY HYDROGEN
A proton and a neutron combine to create a nucleus of "heavy hydrogen", hydrogen-2 or deuterium. Some deuterium nuclei escape further reactions and are still found in the Universe today.

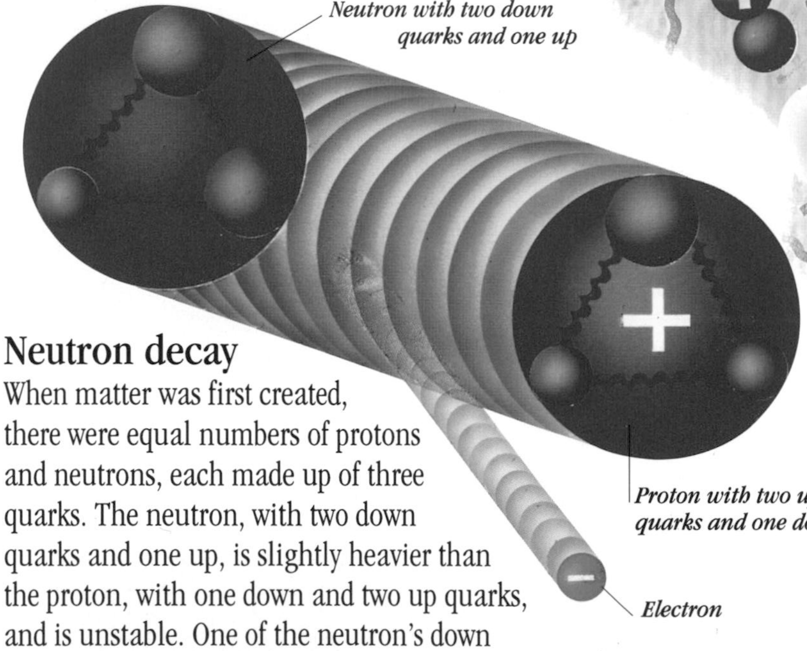

Neutron with two down quarks and one up

Neutron decay

When matter was first created, there were equal numbers of protons and neutrons, each made up of three quarks. The neutron, with two down quarks and one up, is slightly heavier than the proton, with one down and two up quarks, and is unstable. One of the neutron's down quarks decays into an up, giving off a negatively charged electron and a neutral antineutrino (not shown here) in the process. The result is that the neutron turns into a proton.

Proton with two up quarks and one down

Electron

PROTONS ON THE RAMPAGE

At the end of the first second, neutrons began to decay into protons. Proton numbers went on the increase, and by the time the first elements started to form — when the temperature had cooled to 900 million °C (1,600 million °F) — there were seven protons to every neutron.

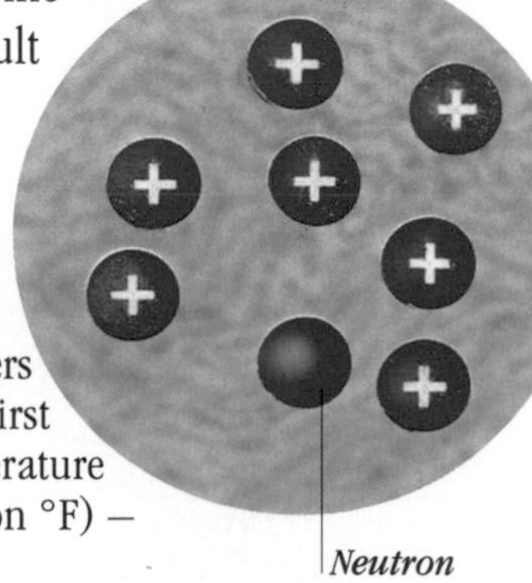

Neutron

COSMIC MASTERCHEF

To Russian-American physicist George Gamow — who conceived the Big Bang theory as we now know it — the early Universe was a primordial cauldron. In the late 1940s, he and his colleagues proposed that the elements were created during a very early period of the expanding Universe. They also predicted that there would be an "afterglow" arising from this hot, early phase, bathing the whole Universe. The prediction was forgotten — until the afterglow was discovered almost 20 years later.

George Gamow (1904-1968) was also a great popularizer of science, wrote poetry, and did research in genetics.

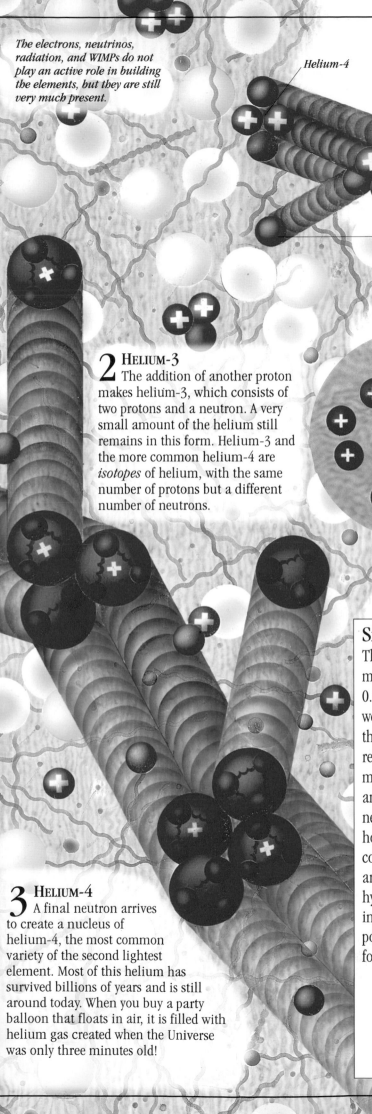

The electrons, neutrinos, radiation, and WIMPs do not play an active role in building the elements, but they are still very much present.

Neutron

Helium-4

Lithium-7

Neutron

Proton

4 LAST AND LEAST — LITHIUM

By the end of the first three minutes, the frenzy of element creation is almost over. There is just time for one final reaction. A few helium-4 nuclei acquire a proton and two neutrons, producing small amounts of the isotope of the third lightest element, lithium. While the temperature is still high enough for nuclear fusion, the continuing expansion will drive the nuclei, protons, and neutrons too far apart to produce any more elements.

2 HELIUM-3

The addition of another proton makes helium-3, which consists of two protons and a neutron. A very small amount of the helium still remains in this form. Helium-3 and the more common helium-4 are *isotopes* of helium, with the same number of protons but a different number of neutrons.

Helium-4

Mopping up the neutrons

The creation of the elements (nucleosynthesis) had the effect of mopping up all the neutrons and tying them up in nuclei, almost entirely helium. This also stabilized the neutrons, preventing them from decaying into protons. Some of the protons also ended up in nuclei, but they were so numerous that most protons remained free – as hydrogen nuclei. As a result, the Universe should have ended up with ten times more hydrogen than helium. Put another way, helium – which is heavier than hydrogen – should make up about a quarter of the mass of the Universe today.

Sifting through the ashes

The "ashes" of the Big Bang – the elements created in its first three minutes – should work out as 77% hydrogen, 23% helium, and 0.000,000,1% lithium, according to detailed calculations. How can we check if the composition of the cosmos matches up? Our part of the Galaxy has suffered "pollution" by elements produced more recently in stars. But some gas clouds far out in space consist of material virtually unaltered since the Big Bang. By analysing the light from these gas clouds, or nebulae, astronomers can find exactly how much of each element they contain. The answer is that there are tiny amounts of lithium, while hydrogen and helium come in at 77% and 23% – powerful evidence for the Big Bang.

3 HELIUM-4

A final neutron arrives to create a nucleus of helium-4, the most common variety of the second lightest element. Most of this helium has survived billions of years and is still around today. When you buy a party balloon that floats in air, it is filled with helium gas created when the Universe was only three minutes old!

The Orion Nebula is a glowing cloud of hydrogen and helium in which stars have just been born.

Echoes of the Big Bang

AFTER ITS BUSY FIRST THREE MINUTES, when particles came and went and the first elements were forged, the Universe settled down to a much calmer period. It lasted more than a quarter of a million years. The ingredients of the cosmos stayed the same, merely becoming ever more dilute as the Universe continued to expand. The main component was radiation, continually bouncing off the particles of matter to form an impenetrable luminous fog. But one day, the fog abruptly cleared. The echoes of that momentous event still survive as a background of heat radiation filling the Universe. It is powerful evidence that the Big Bang really did happen.

Universe clears

Three hundred thousand years after the Big Bang, the Universe suddenly changed from being an opaque fireball into the clear, transparent cosmos we live in today. The key to the change was heat — or rather, the lack of heat in the expanding and ever-cooling Universe. Once the temperature had dropped to about 3,000°C (5,500°F) — about half the temperature of the Sun's surface — matter formed itself into atoms, which allow radiation to pass unhindered.

The darker regions are where dark matter is beginning to clump together.

DOMINATED BY RADIATION

A slice through the early Universe reveals a uniform fog of radiation. At first, it was mainly in the form of energetic gamma rays; as the cosmos cooled, it changed to X-rays and, ultimately, light and heat (infrared radiation). Because the radiation kept the electrons apart from the protons and helium nuclei, this is called the "radiation-dominated era". Dark matter, in the form of WIMPs and/or neutrinos, was unaffected by radiation and began to clump together by gravity.

THE FOGGY, FOGGY UNIVERSE

Seen on the smallest scales, the hot, early Universe was a seething pot-pourri of dark matter, radiation, atomic nuclei, and electrons. In particular, the electrons and photons were constantly in battle with each other. Photons and electrons parried continuously, and neither got anywhere. Photons would bounce off one electron, only to collide with another, then another. Because light is carried by photons, light could never travel in a straight line — and as a result, the Universe was opaque.

Hydrogen nucleus: a single proton

Electron

Helium nucleus: two protons and two neutrons

Photons cannot travel in straight lines, so you would not be able to see more than a fraction of a millimetre.

The "last scattering surface" — the "wall" dividing the opaque from the transparent Universe.

Photons and electrons were constantly colliding in the high temperatures left after the Big Bang. For 300,000 years, the Universe was foggy.

SUDDEN CLEARING

As the Universe cooled, the electrons moved more slowly and found it more and more difficult to resist being attracted to the positive electric charge of the protons and other nuclei. When the temperature dropped to 3,000°C (5,500°F), they were pulled into orbit around the nuclei to form the first atoms of hydrogen, helium, and lithium. Once the electrons were locked up in atoms, they lost the freedom to hinder the passing photons. Light had a free passage – and space became transparent.

The first atoms form: hydrogen (one proton and one electron) and helium (two protons, two neutrons, and two electrons).

Light (blue wiggly line) is not affected by the bound electrons, and travels unimpeded through the Universe.

After the clearing, the "matter-dominated" era begins – and has continued to the present day. Clumps of dark matter start to attract the hydrogen-helium gas around them, forming huge clouds that will eventually become galaxies.

Radiation from the "last scattering surface" travels far into the future. As the Universe expands, the radiation cools down, changing from heat and light to radio waves.

FINDING THE AFTERGLOW

In the early 1960s, physicists Arno Penzias and Robert Wilson started to search for faint radio signals, called microwaves, from the outskirts of our Galaxy. For this, they chose a particularly sensitive radio telescope, a 6-metre (20-ft) horn antenna at Holmdel, New Jersey. But it seemed to be bedevilled with interference – a constant signal from all over the sky, corresponding to radiation at a temperature of −270°C (−454°F or 3 degrees above absolute zero). They thought the signal arose from pigeon droppings in the telescope, but colleagues realized that this "microwave background" was the hot afterglow of the Big Bang, now cooled down by the expansion of the Universe. It was the clinching evidence that the Universe began in a hot Big Bang.

Penzias and Wilson next to the antenna with which they discovered the background of heat radiation.

THE SAME IN ALL DIRECTIONS

Wherever you are on Earth you look outward into space, and backward in time. That's because all radiation, including light and radio waves, takes time to reach you. Look a short distance into space, and you are surrounded by nearby stars a few light years away. A larger telescope picks out galaxies as they were millions of years ago, and a larger one still can detect quasars billions of years ago. The most distant radiation a telescope can detect comes from the "last scattering surface" – the "wall" where the heat radiation escapes from the early fog. Whatever direction it points, the telescope can see back in time to this "wall". As a result, the background of heat radiation comes to us with equal intensity from all directions.

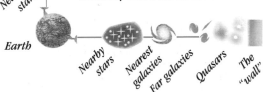

When we detect the microwave background, we are looking back to 300,000 years after the Big Bang. We cannot see any farther back, because before then the Universe was opaque.

Ripples in space

AFTER THE COSMIC FOG CLEARED, at an age of 300,000 years, the stage was set for a major change. Radiation was still around in vast abundance, but it was no longer boss. Matter now started to control its own fate, under the ruling force of its own gravity. Atoms of hydrogen and helium pulled on each other, and both felt the gravitational pull of the dark matter (WIMPs and/or neutrinos). Over hundreds of millions of years, the gas coagulated into clouds, like milk curdling into cheese. Our evidence for these events is a faint pattern of ripples in the background heat radiation.

The Cosmic Background Explorer (COBE) carried three telescopes tuned into heat radiation left over from the Big Bang.

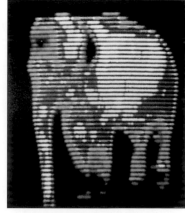

A "heat image" shows which parts of an elephant are a few degrees hotter or colder. COBE measured differences a million times smaller.

Cosmic thermometer

If the matter in the early, expanding Universe had been the same temperature and density everywhere, the gas would have spread out ever more thinly, and the Universe today would consist only of rarefied gas. In fact, it contains galaxies, stars, and planets. The seeds of these clumps of matter must have been sown in the original dense fog, imprinting a pattern of cooler patches in the heat radiation from this era. From the mid-1960s, astronomers searched in vain for these elusive ripples. Success came in 1992, with the COBE satellite. It was the world's most sensitive thermometer, built to probe the chill temperatures of deep space.

HEAT OF THE NIGHT

In COBE's heat image of the entire sky, the coloured ripples reveal regions that are just a few millionths of a degree hotter (pink) or colder (blue) than average. The denser patches appear blue because the radiation cools as it escapes from the greater gravitational pull.

Denser regions of gas (blue in COBE's map) pull together by their own gravity. In between, low density (pink) regions expand to become empty voids.

The gases detected by COBE lie so far away that they show the Universe as it was almost 13 billion years ago, just 300,000 years after the Big Bang.

The warm and cooler ripples show how gas from the original fireball was starting to break up into denser patches.

Expanding picture

This is the story of one region of the Universe, from its portrait in the COBE map through to the clumps of gas forming long strings, known as filaments, that would condense into the first galaxies. Between lie vast voids of empty space, some more than a hundred million light years across.

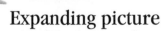

GROWING VOIDS AND FILAMENTS

The Universe 300 million years after the Big Bang resembled a piece of Swiss cheese. Clusters of galaxies had formed from the denser clumps of gas. They lay in long filaments surrounding empty voids. Where filaments met, the galaxies swarm in denser congregations, called superclusters. From this point, the Universe simply expanded, giving rise to the distribution of galaxies we observe today.

COBE has revealed why galaxies today are spread out as filaments surrounding voids.

The longest filaments are called "walls" of galaxies.

The voids contain few galaxies.

Some astronomers think the gas clouds were marshalled into filaments by the gravity of cosmic strings, surviving from the earliest moments of the Universe.

The dots show the distribution of hydrogen and helium gases, starting to turn into galaxies.

WHERE IS THE DARK MATTER TODAY?

Astronomers do not know how the dark matter is spread now. It could be clumped together with the galaxies, or spread more evenly between the filaments and voids.

The route to galaxy birth

Two competing theories describe how COBE's "curdled" lumps of gas came to form galaxies grouped into clusters and super-clusters. In each case, the basic ingredients are the hydrogen and helium gases from the Big Bang, condensing under the gravitational influence of the dark matter. If most of the dark matter consists of neutrinos, it leads to the "top down" theory of galaxy formation; if WIMPs predominate, we get the "bottom up" version of events.

TOP DOWN THEORY

According to the "top down" theory, huge filaments of gas split into smaller clouds, which then split again. The filaments define the size and shape of the final superclusters and clusters, well before each small gas cloud turns into an individual galaxy.

BOTTOM UP THEORY

According to the "bottom up" theory, huge numbers of galaxies were born very soon after the period seen by COBE. At first, these galaxies were scattered randomly, but gravity then pulled them together to make clusters and superclusters.

SEARCHING FOR SMALLER RIPPLES

These miniature radio telescopes in the Canary Islands are looking for smaller ripples than COBE detected to discover more precisely how galaxies, including our own Milky Way, were born from the cosmic fireball. Along with other sensitive telescopes at locations ranging from Antarctica to high-flying balloons, the radio horns are designed to discover ripples small enough to have been the seeds of galaxies.

Birth of the Milky Way

Astronomers can date when the big bang took place, but can only guess that the galaxies formed about half a billion years later. Their instruments cannot record the subtle coming together of gas clouds that resulted in the creation of billions of galaxies. Fortunately, youthful galaxies undergo violent outbursts that can be witnessed halfway across the Universe – but after that, they settle down. And that's lucky for us, for we live in such a galaxy. This is the story of our Milky Way from its own birth to the day it created the Sun and planets.

Our Galaxy is born as countless warm gas clouds come together under the pull of gravity. Stars are born as clouds collide.

A great deal of gas starts to accumulate in the galaxy's core. Its gravity becomes so great that a massive black hole forms and grows.

Gas and stars spiral into the black hole, forming a superhot whirlpool called an accretion disc. This brilliant disc is a quasar.

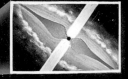

Cross-section of the quasar's accretion disc and its high-speed jets

A violent youth

In its youth, the centre of our Galaxy probably flared into life as a quasar. A quasar is the tiny, dazzling core of a very young and active galaxy. At its heart is a supermassive black hole, voraciously gobbling gas – and shooting what it doesn't eat far out into space. Astronomers have found thousands of quasars, most so remote they look like very faint stars.

The jets from a radio galaxy billow out into huge clouds.

A quasar sends out two jets of charged particles at almost the speed of light.

The quasar has evolved into a radio galaxy

A CHANGING UNIVERSE

When astronomers look out to great distances, they are looking back in time, to the Universe as it was in its youth. They find that many more distant galaxies have quasars at their core than nearby galaxies. So the Universe is changing with time, as the Big Bang theory predicts. This rules out theories that suggest the Universe is infinitely old and unchanging.

Quasar

The early Universe (small sphere) contains many more quasars and radio galaxies than the Universe of today (large sphere).

MARTIN RYLE

In the late 1950s, the British astronomer Martin Ryle (1918-1984) used a radio telescope that he and his team had built at Cambridge to look at galaxies in the distant Universe. He came up with the first evidence that galaxies were more tightly packed together in the past, and that the young Universe was dominated by quasars.

GROWING LESS VIOLENT

Our Galaxy's quasar phase lasted for only a few million years. Next, it embarked on a less violent phase, as a radio galaxy. The jets it beamed out as a quasar billowed out into two enormous clouds, generating powerful radio waves. There was still potential for outbursts from the core – the black hole was there, lurking – but as gas was used up to make stars, the black hole was slowly starved.

The radio-emitting jets can span more than a million light years.

SETTLING DOWN

Nine billion years after its fiery birth, our Milky Way was starting to settle down. A huge black hole, weighing in at three million star masses, still lurked at its core; but it was quiescent, for gas fodder was not as plentiful as before. The Galaxy had by now given birth to billions of stars, arranged in a beautiful spiral shape 100,000 light years across. But there was always room for more.

Pillars of starbirth: young stars emerging from a pillar of dust and gas in the Eagle Nebula about 7,000 years ago.

A STAR IS BORN

Some 4.6 billion years ago, a cloud of dust and gas started to collapse in an anonymous suburb of the Milky Way. As it shrank, it spun faster, eventually becoming a disc. At its heart, it grew hotter and denser, until the core flashed into life. A star, our Sun, had been born. Powered by nuclear fusion reactions, the young Sun showered light and energy onto its emerging family: the nine planets forming in the surrounding disc.

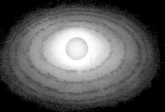

The young Sun forms in a disc of gas and dust.

The surrounding disc condenses into the planets, including Earth.

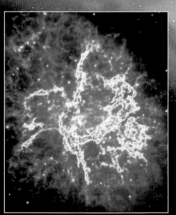

Crab Nebula: the remains of a dying star that blasted heavy elements across space.

STARTING WITH HYDROGEN...

All stars can combine the nuclei of hydrogen in their cores to make helium, a reaction that gives out energy. The heavier stars can also fuse three heliums to create carbon.

The heavy gang

George Gamow believed that all the elements were created in the Big Bang. But now we know that it made only the lightest — hydrogen, helium, and lithium. It turns out that the other 89 elements, making up just 1% of the total material in the Universe, were forged in the nuclear furnaces of stars. They were then scattered throughout space by stars shedding matter in their death throes.

... ENDING WITH IRON

Massive stars can create elements as heavy as iron in their cores. When they try to fuse iron, they explode as supernovas, blasting their outer layers into space. In the fury of the explosion, even heavier elements can be synthesized.

Three helium nuclei combine to form carbon.

Each helium nucleus consists of two protons and two neutrons.

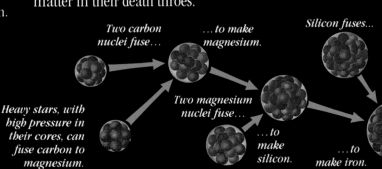

Heavy stars, with high pressure in their cores, can fuse carbon to magnesium.

Two carbon nuclei fuse...

...to make magnesium.

Two magnesium nuclei fuse...

...to make silicon.

Silicon fuses...

...to make iron.

The heaviest stars can fuse two nuclei of silicon to make iron.

Creation myths

WHEN THE UNIVERSE reached 9 billion years, a small and undistinguished planet was born. At first, it was a hot, violent world; but as it cooled, life somehow arose and gained a stronghold. First plants, then animals, and finally humans appeared on the scene. They exploded into scores of different cultures. But common to each were the questions: "Where did we come from?" and "How did it all begin?". The first ideas on creation ranged from the wildly romantic Aztec myths to the pragmatic Judaeo-Christian approach.

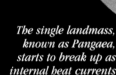

Meteorite impacts blast its surface.

Earth forms from cloud of dust and gas.

Clouds cloak Earth, later condensing as rain which creates oceans in low-lying regions.

The single landmass, known as Pangaea, starts to break up as internal heat currents break the crust apart.

EVOLUTION OF EARTH
Earth was born from millions of rocky fragments, formed from tiny particles of dust around the young Sun. More rocky fragments, meteorites, bombarded the surface, heating it until it glowed. As the hot and molten surface cooled, water vapour condensed as clouds and then filled the oceans. The thin crust of rock split into continents, pushed around by currents of molten rock within the planet

Seven days of creation
According to Christians, "In the beginning, God created the Heaven and the Earth". Over the next six days, God worked hard on his creation: establishing day and night, seas, land, and plants by day three; the stars, Sun and Moon, sea creatures, and birds by day five. On the sixth day, he made animals and the pinnacle of his creation, humans. He set aside the seventh day for rest – which is why Sunday is holy to Christians.

God, having created Heaven and Earth, marvels at his handiwork.

Atum has spoken
The Ancient Egyptians, whose civilization lasted for more than two millennia, wove many intricate myths. They believed that the Universe began when the god Atum came into being, simply by calling his own name. Next, Atum vomited up his brother and sister, Shu and Tefnut, who in turn gave birth to the god Geb (who symbolized the Earth) and the goddess Nut (the sky). All the people of Egypt were descended from the children of Nut and Geb. The whole act of creation was watched over by the all-seeing, non-interfering Eye.

In Egyptian mythology, the lovers Geb (the Earth) and Nut (the sky) are separated from one another so that the day can take place. At night they are reunited.

THEORY REPLACES MYTH
In the 20th century, discoveries of the expanding Universe, a background of heat radiation, and the amount of hydrogen and helium in the cosmos have given us a theory – not a myth – of the origin of the Universe, as summarized on the fold out pages underneath this page. But we may never know *why* the Universe began.

Cosmic egg

The Chinese Universe began with a huge cosmic egg, containing *yin-yang*. This comprised everything and its exact opposite: male-female, cold-heat, dark-light. Within the *yin-yang* was the god Phan Ku: his eyes became the Sun and Moon; his breath the wind; his hair the trees and plants; his flesh the Earth; his sweat rain, and eventually the worms that left his rotting body turned into people.

In another version of the Chinese creation myth Pan-Kou-Che, the Creator, chips away at his great work among the swirling clouds.

Quetzalcoatl and Tezcatlipoca

The Aztecs of Mexico had many creation legends. One concerns the gods Quetzalcoatl and Tezcatlipoca, who pulled the goddess Coatlicue down from the heavens and ripped her in two – creating the sky and the Earth. Her body became mountains and valleys; her hair turned into plants. But Coatlicue was unhappy at her treatment and demanded frequent sacrifices of human hearts.

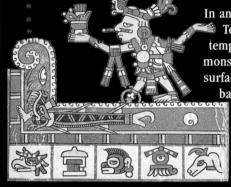

In another myth, Tezcatlipoca tempts a water monster to the surface. She is badly injured, and her body becomes the Earth.

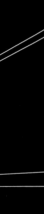

Vishnu, one of the Hindu gods associated with creation.

Prajapati and the golden egg

Several of the creation myths in the Hindu culture feature gods coming into being by uttering their names. Others describe great oceans, and a few involve cosmic eggs. One such legend concerns an ocean that gave birth to a golden egg. After a year, Prajapati emerged from the egg. He rested on the shell for another year before trying to speak. The first sound he made became the Earth; the second, the sky; and the third, the seasons.

Earth's continents today are still on the move, driven by currents of rock deep below. Their separation has led to forms of life and human cultures that are unique to each continent.

Aboriginal Dreamtime

Central to the Australian Aboriginal culture is "Dreamtime": an era when their ancestors went on journeys, creating "dreamings" that became people, sacred sites, and traditions. The ancestors were often lizards; warmed by the Sun, they become human. The god of the Dieri Aboriginals made the first human in the form of a lizard, but found it could only walk when its tail had been cut off. The Dreamtime ancestors are celebrated in dramatic rock paintings.

Dreamtime: two of the Aboriginals' magical flying ancestors, who created sacred sites and creatures where they touched down.

Scale of space

BEFORE PEOPLE COULD UNDERSTAND the history of the Universe, they first had to work out its geography. But plumbing the depths of space was not easy: objects in the sky looked as if they were all at the same distance, pinned to the great dome of the sky. Fortunately, the Moon and planets gave away their relative closeness by virtue of their movement. By the 17th century, astronomers had realized that the Sun was the centre of the Solar System and began to measure the distances to planets. Two centuries later, they extended the tape measure to the nearest stars, almost a million times farther away. Early in the 20th century, they identified individual stars in distant galaxies and could extend the ladder of cosmic distances more than a million times farther.

PARALLAX WORKS FOR UP TO 300 LIGHT YEARS

A nearby object appears to shift against a distant background when viewed from two positions – that's the principle behind parallax. If you know the length of the "baseline" between the two positions, and can measure the shift, it is simple geometry to calculate the object's distance. This method works for stars up to 300 light years away.

Earth's position in December

In parallax measurements, the baseline is the diameter of Earth's orbit, equal to 2 AU.

Earth's position in J[...]

Scale of the Universe

From planets to the remotest galaxies, astronomers can measure the distance to any object. They use a "ladder" of methods – planetary speeds, parallax, Cepheid stars, and whole galaxies. Each depends on the previous step, so distances grow increasingly uncertain: the farthest galaxies may be 30 per cent nearer or farther than estimated.

PTOLEMAIC THEORY

The Ancient Greeks believed that the Sun, Moon, and planets circled the Earth. To explain the fact that planets sometimes travel backwards in the sky, the Greeks thought each moved in a small circle (an epicycle) that was itself orbiting Earth. Ptolemy summarized the theory in the *Almagest*, written in the 2nd century AD.

COPERNICAN THEORY

The Ptolemaic theory held sway until 1543, when the Polish monk Nicolaus Copernicus suggested that the Sun lay at the centre of things. The Church, however, taught that the Earth was central: his theory was heresy. Perhaps this is why he did not publish it until the day he died.

The edge of the Milky Way lies 50,000 ly away. This "non-linear" scale makes the stars seem more crowded at the edge. Viewed normally, the centre of the Galaxy is the most dense.

Beta Centauri
460 ly

WITHIN THE SOLAR SYSTEM

Astronomers find the distance to planets from the speed they orbit the Sun. Those nearest the Sun move fastest to avoid being pulled in by its gravity. Mercury, 58 million km (36 million miles) from the Sun, speeds around at 48 km/sec (30 miles/sec). Pluto, almost a hundred times farther out, travels at a leisurely [...] km/sec (2.9 miles/sec). The Earth's distance from the Sun – the astronomical unit (AU) – is the first step in a long ladder of distances.

Alpha and Beta Centauri appear to be of similar brightness in the sky, but brilliant Beta is 100 times farther away.

Alpha Centauri
4.3 ly

Earth

Pluto
49.3 AU

100 ly

1 ly

Earth to Sun is 149.6 million km or 1 AU.

LIGHT YEARS AWAY

Astronomers describe the huge distances to the stars in terms of light years. Light moves at 300,000 km/sec (186,000 miles/sec), and in a year it travels 9.5 trillion km (5.9 trillion miles), or 1 light year (ly). It equals 63,240 AU. The nearest star, Alpha Centauri, lies 40 trillion km (25 trillion miles) away – 4.3 ly. Most of the stars we can see with the naked eye in the sky are within 1,000 ly.

Extragalactic distances

Most galaxies lie millions of light years away. Astronomers measure their distances by comparing the apparent brightness of their most luminous stars, the supergiants, with supergiants in our own Galaxy. For more remote galaxies, they compare the brightness of globular star clusters – or the whole galaxy – with nearby examples. Distances to the farthest clusters of galaxies are estimated by measuring the apparent brightness of their biggest members.

The Coma Cluster is a cluster of 5,000 or more galaxies lying 300 million ly away. It lies at the centre of a supercluster, containing millions of galaxies.

Apparent shift in position between June and December

A nearby star (above left) will show a bigger parallax shift than a more distant star (above right) when viewed from opposite sides of the Earth's orbit.

The Virgo Cluster is the nearest giant swarm of galaxies, with more than 2,000 members.

Virgo Cluster
50 million ly

The Andromeda Galaxy is the closest major galaxy. It is half as large again as the Milky Way, and is the farthest object visible to the naked eye.

Andromeda Galaxy
2.3 million ly

100 million ly

MORE DISTANT SHORES
Astronomers can measure distances to clusters of galaxies billions of light years away. Many galaxies in clusters are much bigger and more luminous than our Milky Way, and can be seen at these vast distances. The light takes so long to reach the Earth, that astronomers are seeing the farthest clusters as they were before the Sun and its planets were born.

Edge of Milky Way 50,000 ly

Large Magellanic Cloud 170,000 ly

1 million ly

Globular clusters up to 100,000 ly

Small Magellanic Cloud 190,000 ly

10,000 ly

The Large and Small Magellanic Clouds are the closest galaxies to us. They orbit the Milky Way and are visible to the naked eye.

The Cepheid yardstick

In 1912, American astronomer Henrietta Leavitt (1868-1921) was studying Cepheid variables – stars that oscillate in brightness in regular cycles – in the Small Magellanic Cloud. She discovered that the length of the cycle revealed a Cepheid's true brightness. Hence they are standard candles, which can be used to measure the distances to other galaxies containing Cepheids.

Henrietta Leavitt worked at the Harvard College Observatory, USA.

STANDARD CANDLES
If two stars are putting out the same amount of light but one appears a hundred times dimmer, it must lie ten times farther away. In reality, stars have different luminosities, but astronomers have identified stars such as Cepheids and supergiants that shine with the same brightness. The brightness of the globular clusters of stars surrounding galaxies can also be used as standard candles.

10 ly   20 ly   30 ly   40 ly   50 ly   60 ly   70 ly   80 ly   90 ly   100 ly

1 ly

COSMIC TAPE MEASURE
The Universe is so vast that it is difficult to represent on a page. Here, we have used a non-linear scale that is increasingly compressed: each major division is 100 times more compressed than the previous one.

The Cepheid cycle

Shrinking and dimmest

Expanding and brightest

Largest

Smallest

WHY CEPHEIDS ARE IMPORTANT
Cepheids are thousands of times brighter than the Sun and this, coupled with their cycle of brightening and dimming, makes them easy to recognize in distant galaxies. An astronomer finds the true brightness of a Cepheid from the time it takes to change from bright to dim and back to bright. Comparing that star's apparent with its true brightness gives the distance to its parent galaxy.

Galaxies on the move

TWO BREAKTHROUGHS IN OUR UNDERSTANDING of the Universe came in the 1920s, thanks to American astronomer Edwin Hubble. For centuries, astronomers believed the Milky Way comprised the entire Universe. Hubble was among the first to realize that some of the fuzzy patches, or "nebulae", in the sky were galaxies far beyond our own. His second breakthrough came in 1929. By spreading out the light from each galaxy into a spectrum, he could work out what it was made of and how fast it was moving. To his surprise, most of the galaxies were moving away from ours. There was nothing repulsive about our Galaxy: it was just that the Universe itself was expanding.

When a galaxy is receding, its light waves are stretched. The spectral lines move towards longer, redder wavelengths, and you measure a redshift.

When you spread light from a stationary galaxy into a spectrum, you see dark bands (spectral lines) at particular wavelengths.

When a galaxy approaches you, its light waves are compressed. Its spectral lines move towards shorter, bluer wavelengths and you measure a blueshift.

COSMIC SPEEDOMETER
If sound or light waves are radiating from a moving object, the waves in front become bunched together, while those behind trail. This is the Doppler effect, familiar to everyone who has heard the high pitch of an ambulance siren approaching, and the lower pitch of it receding. The faster it goes, the bigger the change in pitch.

Expanding Universe
The vast majority of galaxies, with the exception of a few nearby ones such as Andromeda, are moving away from us. The galaxies themselves are not moving, it is the space between them that stretches as the Universe expands. In these successive snapshots of the expanding Universe, we see the light from three other galaxies travelling to reach the Milky Way. The more distant the galaxy, the more expanding space lies between the galaxy and us, so the faster it is moving. The higher speed produces a larger redshift in the galaxy's light.

EXPANSIVE ASTRONOMER
Edwin Hubble qualified as a brilliant lawyer before turning to astronomy. His outstanding astronomical contributions were made at the Mount Wilson telescope overlooking Los Angeles in California, often in collaboration with Milton Humason – a former mule driver up to the mountaintop telescope.

Edwin Hubble (1889-1953) in whose honour the Hubble Space Telescope is named.

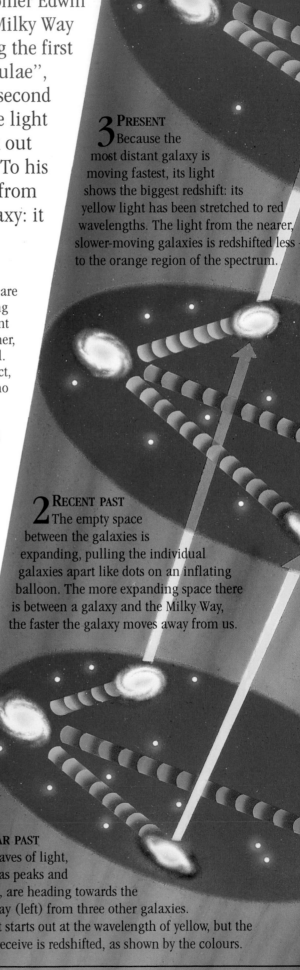

3 PRESENT Because the most distant galaxy is moving fastest, its light shows the biggest redshift: its yellow light has been stretched to red wavelengths. The light from the nearer, slower-moving galaxies is redshifted less – to the orange region of the spectrum.

2 RECENT PAST The empty space between the galaxies is expanding, pulling the individual galaxies apart like dots on an inflating balloon. The more expanding space there is between a galaxy and the Milky Way, the faster the galaxy moves away from us.

1 FAR PAST Waves of light, shown as peaks and troughs, are heading towards the Milky Way (left) from three other galaxies. The light starts out at the wavelength of yellow, but the light we receive is redshifted, as shown by the colours.

As space expands, the galaxies are pulled apart from one another. Note that all the galaxies are moving apart from one another. If you lived on any of these galaxies, you would think you were at the centre of the expanding Universe.

HUBBLE'S LAW

Hubble measured the redshift (which gave the speeds) and brightness (which gave the distance) of many galaxies. When he drew up a graph of the redshift against the distance, he found that the galaxies lay on a straight line: the speed at which they were receding was proportional to the distance. This discovery is enshrined as Hubble's Law. The expansion rate, the Hubble Constant, is being measured ever more precisely: it is now thought to be about 20 km/sec (12 miles/sec) for each 1 million light years.

The amount a galaxy's dark spectral lines shift towards the red wavelengths indicates the speed the galaxy is moving away from us.

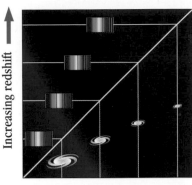

The smaller and dimmer a galaxy looks, the farther away it must lie.

Increasing redshift →

Decreasing brightness →

WINDING THE FILM BACKWARDS

After Hubble discovered the expansion of space in 1929, astronomers were prompted to "wind the film backwards": if the process of expansion is reversed, it leads to the conclusion that the Universe began in an explosion. The rate of expansion, the Hubble Constant, tells you how long ago the explosion occurred. Early estimates of the expansion rate were high, giving an age that was younger than the Earth. Nonetheless, during the next 20 years most astronomers came to believe the Universe began in some kind of Big Bang.

Steady state theory

The idea that the Universe had a definite beginning did not appeal to all astronomers. In 1948, Fred Hoyle, Hermann Bondi, and Tommy Gold came up with the Steady State theory. For them, the Universe had no beginning, and no end. Although expanding, it stayed in perfect balance – like a washing-up bowl that is kept topped-up to overflowing by a trickle from a tap. The "tap", in this case, is the continuous creation of matter from energy – at the paltry rate of about 1 atom per cubic kilometre of space per hour.

PAST

According to the Steady State theory, the Universe should remain unchanging over time, even though it is expanding. This is a view of the Universe at one instant of time: it is evenly spread with 18 galaxies.

PRESENT

This is a view of the same part of the Universe. There are 18 galaxies, but they are not all the same ones. The original galaxies have moved apart as the Universe expanded, and newly formed galaxies (coded orange) have appeared in between.

Most famous of the Steady State trio is the British cosmologist and astrophysicist Fred Hoyle, who first worked out how stars make new elements. He also writes science fiction.

Hermann Bondi (1919-)

Fred Hoyle (1915-)

Tommy Gold (1920-)

FUTURE

Later still, and the scene remains essentially unchanged. More of the original galaxies (coded white) have been carried out of the frame by expansion. But new galaxies (coded green) have formed to take their place.

WHY THE STEADY STATE WILL NOT WORK

The most controversial aspect of the Steady State theory was its dependence on continuous creation: even though the amounts were tiny, it defied the laws of physics. The theory was dealt a fatal blow in 1965, when the background of cosmic heat radiation was discovered. With its extreme smoothness, it is hard to believe it is anything other than the afterglow of the Big Bang. But even before, there were doubts. The abundance of helium exactly fitted Big Bang predictions. And radio astronomers had found that galaxies were more crowded together in the past, meaning that the Universe was not unchanging.

How old is the Universe?

TODAY, THE VAST MAJORITY OF ASTRONOMERS agree on the origin of the Universe: all the evidence points towards a hot Big Bang. The controversy in the 1950s and 1960s about *how* everything began – in a Big Bang or as an unchanging Steady State – has been replaced by one about *when* the Universe started. The answer is now within reach. Despite newspaper headlines claiming that astronomers have discovered stars older than the Universe, several different methods of measuring the date of the Big Bang are coming to a surprisingly close agreement, given the difficulty of dating something that happened billions of years ago.

Measuring the age of the Universe

Astronomers can measure the age of the Universe in three ways. The first involves "winding back" the expansion of the Universe to find out when it started expanding. The next method is to check meteorites for radioactive elements that have been produced in stars since the Big Bang, and are constantly decaying at a known rate. The third technique involves studying stars in old clusters in the Milky Way, born soon after the Universe itself. None of these methods is absolutely precise, but the overlap in their answers is itself strong evidence that the Universe had a definite starting point. Taking an average of all three puts the age of the Universe at 13 billion years.

GRAVITY APPLIES THE BRAKES

Astronomers cannot age the Universe by simply reversing its current rate of growth, unless they are certain that it has always been expanding at the same rate. In fact, gravity must be slowing down the expansion all the time: the mutual pull of all the galaxies on each other, plus the attraction of dark matter, acts as brakes on the expansion. The amount of dark matter suggested by the theory of inflation (see pages 18-19) gives an age one-third less than you find by simply backtracking the current rate at which galaxies are moving apart.

Assume a constant speed for expansion, and the age of the Universe would be 17 billion years.

Allow for gravitational brakes, and the Universe is 11 billion years old.

As we "wind back" the movie towards the Big Bang, the Universe grows steadily denser and hotter.

The far-seeing eye of the Hubble Space Telescope can detect the farthest galaxies in space. Its main task is to measure the age of the Universe.

Although the galaxies move apart from one another, the gravity of a galaxy stops the stars within it from moving apart.

The Universe today consists of a network of superclusters of galaxies, gradually moving apart.

ACCORDING TO THE HUBBLE CONSTANT

For more than 60 years, astronomers have been trying to measure the rate of the expansion of the Universe (the Hubble Constant) – which tells when the Big Bang took place. Early measurements gave an age that was far too low. Now powerful telescopes can reach many distant galaxies, astronomers are confident that the rate they are measuring is far more accurate. It gives an age of about 11 billion years.

The first estimates of the Hubble Constant were 10 times higher – 200 km/sec (120 miles/sec) every million ly.

The Universe is currently expanding at the rate given by the Hubble Constant – 20 km/sec (12 miles/sec) every million light years (ly).

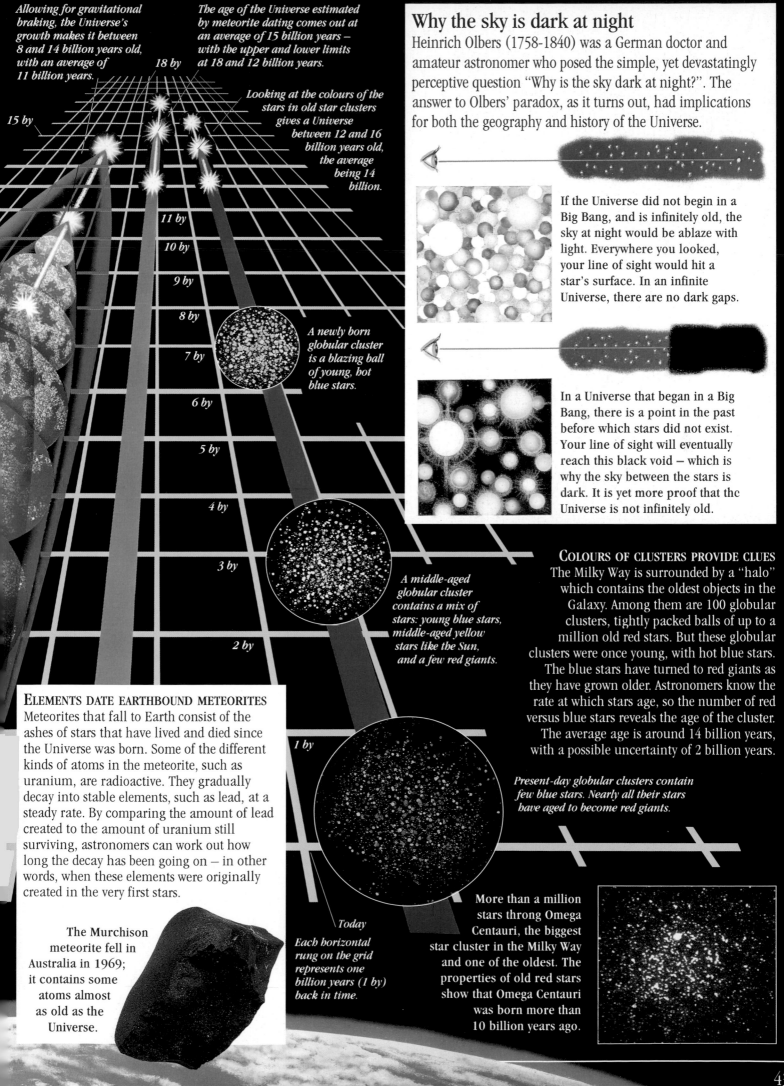

Allowing for gravitational braking, the Universe's growth makes it between 8 and 14 billion years old, with an average of 11 billion years.

The age of the Universe estimated by meteorite dating comes out at an average of 15 billion years – with the upper and lower limits at 18 and 12 billion years.

18 by

15 by

Looking at the colours of the stars in old star clusters gives a Universe between 12 and 16 billion years old, the average being 14 billion.

11 by

10 by

9 by

8 by

7 by

6 by

5 by

4 by

3 by

2 by

1 by

A newly born globular cluster is a blazing ball of young, hot blue stars.

A middle-aged globular cluster contains a mix of stars: young blue stars, middle-aged yellow stars like the Sun, and a few red giants.

Why the sky is dark at night

Heinrich Olbers (1758-1840) was a German doctor and amateur astronomer who posed the simple, yet devastatingly perceptive question "Why is the sky dark at night?". The answer to Olbers' paradox, as it turns out, had implications for both the geography and history of the Universe.

If the Universe did not begin in a Big Bang, and is infinitely old, the sky at night would be ablaze with light. Everywhere you looked, your line of sight would hit a star's surface. In an infinite Universe, there are no dark gaps.

In a Universe that began in a Big Bang, there is a point in the past before which stars did not exist. Your line of sight will eventually reach this black void – which is why the sky between the stars is dark. It is yet more proof that the Universe is not infinitely old.

COLOURS OF CLUSTERS PROVIDE CLUES

The Milky Way is surrounded by a "halo" which contains the oldest objects in the Galaxy. Among them are 100 globular clusters, tightly packed balls of up to a million old red stars. But these globular clusters were once young, with hot blue stars. The blue stars have turned to red giants as they have grown older. Astronomers know the rate at which stars age, so the number of red versus blue stars reveals the age of the cluster. The average age is around 14 billion years, with a possible uncertainty of 2 billion years.

Present-day globular clusters contain few blue stars. Nearly all their stars have aged to become red giants.

ELEMENTS DATE EARTHBOUND METEORITES

Meteorites that fall to Earth consist of the ashes of stars that have lived and died since the Universe was born. Some of the different kinds of atoms in the meteorite, such as uranium, are radioactive. They gradually decay into stable elements, such as lead, at a steady rate. By comparing the amount of lead created to the amount of uranium still surviving, astronomers can work out how long the decay has been going on – in other words, when these elements were originally created in the very first stars.

The Murchison meteorite fell in Australia in 1969; it contains some atoms almost as old as the Universe.

*Today
Each horizontal rung on the grid represents one billion years (1 by) back in time.*

More than a million stars throng Omega Centauri, the biggest star cluster in the Milky Way and one of the oldest. The properties of old red stars show that Omega Centauri was born more than 10 billion years ago.

Curved cosmos

WHERE IS THE CENTRE OF THE UNIVERSE? And is there an edge? These two simple questions are among the most difficult to answer. The Universe may be infinite in size, going on forever in all directions, and then it has no edge. In addition, no particular point lies in the "centre". Astronomers call this an open Universe. But in fact space is not that simple. Gravity can distort the shape of space, bending it into an unimaginable fourth dimension. It could even curve right back on itself, as a closed Universe. Scientists are now trying to measure the actual shape of the Universe we live in. It determines how the Universe continues to expand, and how it will eventually end.

Our Universe: the outside view
This is the ultimate bird's-eye view: how our Universe may look to a superior being who lives outside our own space and time. It stretches far beyond the Universe we can observe from the Milky Way. This is an open, infinite Universe, with no centre and no edge, but slightly curved into a fourth dimension. To fit it on the page, we have had to represent a three-dimensional Universe in two dimensions.

The matter that makes up the huge superclusters and filaments of galaxies imposes gentle curves on the overall shape of space.

OUR OBSERVABLE UNIVERSE
Each galaxy is at the centre of its own observable Universe, which is very much smaller than the whole Universe. This is the observable Universe around the Milky Way, stretching 13 billion light years out into space – as far as we can see in the time since the Big Bang took place.

OBSERVABLE UNIVERSE TWO
A galaxy trillions of light years away will also be centred in its own observable Universe. This, too, will be 13 billion light years in radius, bounded in all directions by the Big Bang. But the Milky Way is well over the horizon, just as this galaxy is outside our observable Universe.

ALBERT EINSTEIN ON GRAVITY
In 1915 Albert Einstein (1879-1955) overturned all previous ideas of space and gravity with the publication of his general theory of relativity. This says that a massive body, such as the Earth or a star, bends space near it. We feel this curvature of space as gravity. The theory also predicts that there could be a universal force of repulsion, the "cosmological constant", operating over millions of light years, but there is little evidence that this force really exists.

The greatest scientist of the 20th century, Einstein was unremarkable at school and started work as a patents clerk.

The curved grid lines show the distortion of space by matter.

Empty three-dimensional space can be visualized as a cube.

Put a massive object into space, and the structure becomes distorted.

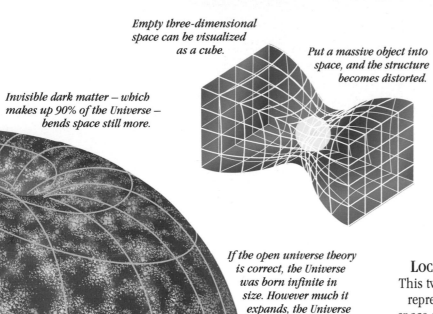

Invisible dark matter – which makes up 90% of the Universe – bends space still more.

Cramming three dimensions into two

Einstein's theory of relativity says that the gravity of an object manifests itself by distorting space. Visualizing space bent by the presence of matter is not easy. The simplest way is to represent three-dimensional space in two dimensions. Imagine empty space as being like a thin rubber sheet on which you place a massive object: it warps the sheet to make a dent, or "gravitational well". The more massive the object, the deeper the well.

If the open universe theory is correct, the Universe was born infinite in size. However much it expands, the Universe is always infinite in extent.

LOCAL BENDING

This two-dimensional representation shows how space can be bent locally. Here, the Earth distorts space into a well in its vicinity, forcing objects to follow the curved gridlines. We feel the effect as gravity.

Where gravity bends space, parallel lines can meet and the angles of a triangle need not add up to 180°. The angles in a triangle drawn around the Earth would add up to more than 180° – but only by one part in a billion.

An open, infinitely large Universe could be saddle-shaped. This is called "negative curvature".

A WARPED UNIVERSE

The Earth's gravitational pull corresponds to only a small distortion in space. More massive objects produce much larger distortions. And the combined mass of all the galaxies and dark matter in the Universe can bend the whole of space into a fourth dimension. We cannot comprehend this curvature, but we can illustrate how a 2-D universe could be bent into the third dimension. According to Einstein's general theory of relativity, this bending can result in three possible shapes, depending on the amount of matter in the Universe.

If there were more matter, the Universe could be completely flat. It is still infinite.

A Universe containing a lot of matter has a "positive curvature". This kind of space could curve back on itself.

The theory of inflation predicts an amount of matter in the Universe that makes it – on the largest scales of all – almost exactly flat.

The "expansion of the Universe" means that space itself has been expanding, pulling galaxies apart from one another.

THE CLOSED UNIVERSE

If there is enough matter in the Universe, space may have enough positive curvature to bend right back on itself. The cosmos we inhabit would then be closed. In this 2-D representation, astronauts exploring a closed Universe would travel right round without finding an edge. Being unaware of a third dimension, they would be unable to locate a centre. For us, living in 3-D space, a closed Universe means curvature into the fourth dimension, with no centre in our Universe.

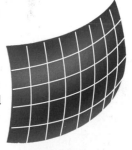

Trillions of years later, the crew aboard a battered rocket awakens to find planet Earth ahead! They have circumnavigated the Universe.

A closed Universe is finite – it does not stretch forever – but it has no edges.

A rocket takes off from present-day Earth in a straight line. The crew, frozen until the rocket reaches an exciting destination, expects to plumb the limits of the cosmos.

Far future

IT MAY APPEAR BOLD, if not downright audacious, to predict the far future of the Universe. Yet this crystal-ball gazing is not as presumptuous as it seems, for the fate of the Universe was sealed at the time of the Big Bang. Once the cosmic clock started ticking, that was that. Crucial parameters that were set during the first few fractions of a second – such as the expansion rate and the amount of dark matter created – determined the Universe's future.

Future of an open Universe

An open Universe will continue to expand and cool forever. It might sound like immortality, but in fact it is a slow, lingering death. Given billions of years, all the stars in all the galaxies will die. Even the supermassive black holes in the centres of the galaxies will not last forever. Ultimately, our frigid dark cosmos will be home to a tiny handful of subatomic particles.

Three fates for the Universe: expansion forever, continuous slowing down, or collapse.

Open Universe

Closed Universe

Critical density Universe

OPEN OR CLOSED FUTURE

The fate of the Universe is inextricably linked to its overall shape (see pages 44-45). If it contains very little matter, the Universe is open: it is infinite in all directions and will expand forever. If there is enough matter to bend space around on itself, the Universe is closed: the Universe will expand but the gravity of the matter will eventually force it to collapse on itself. The theory of inflation predicts a "critical density Universe": one in which there is just enough matter to slow, but not to reverse the inflation.

Today's Milky Way is in its prime. Stars are still being born, and there is plenty of dust and gas around to fuel star birth in the future.

The open Universe after 10 trillion trillion (10^{25}) years: the Milky Way has disintegrated into a graveyard of star corpses – neutron stars, black holes, and white dwarf stars – circling a central supermassive black hole. The corpses eventually plunge into the central black hole, or are flung far out.

It is 1 trillion (10^{12}) years after the Big Bang and the Milky Way has used up all its raw materials. The gas-rich spiral arms have disappeared. Stars are dying; many have already expired.

DEATH OF THE SUN

At 5 billion years of age, our Sun is a middle-aged star. It shines by converting hydrogen to helium in its core – a nuclear reaction that creates energy. But 5 billion years in the future, the Sun will run out of fuel. Its dead core will shrink and heat up, causing its outer layers to billow out and cool. It will swallow up the inner planets Mercury and Venus; and even if it does not swallow the Earth, the heat from its approaching surface will vaporize the oceans and the atmosphere. It will be a certain end for life on Earth.

The end: a dying star that has gently puffed off its distended outer layers. The central core will become a white dwarf.

The closed Universe: after 13 trillion years, expansion will stop and be replaced by collapse. Thirteen billion years before the Big Crunch, the Universe is back to its present size. The supermassive black hole in an ageing Milky Way is surrounded by dying, old red stars.

THE PROTON VANISHES

The future of the open Universe may take rather a different course if one prediction from the Grand Unified Theory (GUT) is correct. It suggests that protons and neutrons are not stable. After 10^{33} years they will start to decay, and objects made of these particles will vanish from the Universe.

X boson

Electron

Positron

The positron annihilates with an electron, producing a burst of radiation.

If protons and neutrons decay, white dwarfs and neutron stars will shrink and disappear in a burst of radiation before the supermassive black holes have evaporated. But the ultimate fate of the Universe is unchanged.

Up quarks

Down quark

The X boson changes the down quark into a positron (antielectron) and an up quark into an antiquark.

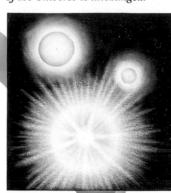

White dwarfs (made of protons, neutrons, and electrons) and neutron stars (made of neutrons) are doomed if protons and neutrons are unstable.

A proton is made of two up quarks and one down. GUT predicts an X boson may appear and live just long enough to change the proton's structure.

The remaining pair of particles, the up quark and the antiquark, quickly annihilate, and the proton vanishes. Neutrons would decay similarly.

Nothing lasts forever. White dwarfs and neutron stars, although obstinately stable, eventually collapse at $10^{10^{77}}$ years to become black holes. These black holes, too, evaporate, ending aeons of existence in a brief burst of radiation.

Even black holes die. They gradually "evaporate", and after some 10^{100} years a supermassive black hole finally disappears in a burst of radiation. According to conventional theories, the surrounding neutron stars and white dwarfs still survive.

The open Universe will exist forever as a bitterly cold, expanding emptiness. A few widely separated electrons and positrons, along with neutrinos and WIMPs, swim in its empty reaches. All are the incredibly distant legacy of the Big Bang.

As the Universe contracts, galaxies begin to merge with each other. Three million years before the Big Crunch, the background radiation has heated up to 20°C (68°F): nights are no longer cold.

With 100,000 years to go to the Big Crunch, the background temperature has risen so much that the sky is hotter than the stars. Stars boil away from the outside.

The Big Crunch

3 minutes to go

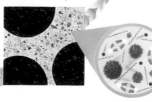

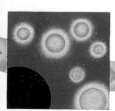

3 million years to go

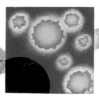

100,000 years to go

In the last three minutes, supermassive black holes at the centres of galaxies merge.

Radiation breaks up the atomic nuclei: before they turn to particle soup, they are swallowed by black holes.

COUNTDOWN TO THE BIG CRUNCH

If there is sufficient matter, its gravitational brakes can consign the Universe to a fiery death in the Big Crunch. The amount of matter dictates just *when* these brakes start to bite. Astronomers do not know how much matter there is, so they cannot say when, if ever, the turning point between expansion and collapse will be reached. But they can calculate what would happen in the countdown to the Big Crunch. It is rather like a reversed Big Bang, but the final instants may differ. While the Big Bang had only mini black holes, the collapsing Universe has supermassive black holes that will survive until the bitter end; the Universe may literally disappear up its own mega black hole.

Other big bangs

WE THINK OF OUR UNIVERSE as being the totality of everything that exists. But if our Universe came into being, why not other universes? If we could step outside our Universe, and dimensions were no problem, we might glimpse a plethora of other universes, populating every dimension. It is a bizarre prediction of modern physics that universes can appear spontaneously, then instantly disappear again. There is nothing to prevent this happening, if the net amount of energy in a universe is zero — a result of the positive energy of all the matter within it being counter-balanced by the negative energy produced by gravity.

Bubbling up from the cosmic foam

If you look at the surface of the ocean from an aeroplane, it looks smooth. But view it from a rowing boat, and the perspective is completely different: there are huge waves, turbulence, and all kinds of violent activity. And it is just the same with space. Seen on the smallest scales of all — around 10^{-33} cm or less than a trillion-trillionth the size of an atom — it seethes and bubbles like billowing foam. This cosmic foam could be the source of countless baby universes that bubble up from nowhere. Most of them start to expand but never get any further; well before they reach even the size of a proton, they contract and vanish within a fraction of a second. Each is a tiny closed universe in its own right. But if a universe manages to undergo inflation — like the blue and green universes here — it is set for a long future.

Suddenly, our Universe inflates enormously, propelling itself into a dramatic phase of accelerated growth. After that, its existence is guaranteed.

Our own Universe (coloured blue) manages to get further than its own siblings, and grows steadily.

The multi-dimensional cosmic foam continually bubbles with baby universes. Most expand for a fraction of a second before collapsing and disappearing.

STEPHEN HAWKING'S UNIVERSE

According to the British physicist Stephen Hawking, the Universe originally consisted of four dimensions of space, but no time dimension — and without time, there could be no change. But spontaneously one of the space dimensions turned into time. This gave the Universe the freedom to change and evolve. In this 2-D representation, the Universe starts with three space dimensions. One turns into time and the Universe can start to expand and spring to life.

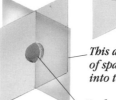

This 2-D universe begins with three dimensions of space and no time dimension. As a result, it is unable to change.

This dimension of space changes into time.

Unchanging universe

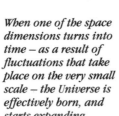

Now the Universe can change and evolve.

When one of the space dimensions turns into time — as a result of fluctuations that take place on the very small scale — the Universe is effectively born, and starts expanding.

Other beginnings

Bubbling from the cosmic foam and Hawking's theory are just two of the ways a universe can be born, according to the latest theories of physics and astronomy. Here are two more ideas as to how new universes might be generated.

OSCILLATING UNIVERSE

A universe may emerge from the wreck of a previous universe like a phoenix rising from the ashes. In the "oscillating universe" theory, a closed universe collapses in a Big Crunch. Instead of just disappearing, the matter and energy bounce back as another Big Bang with completely different properties from its predecessor. The cycle may repeat over and over again.

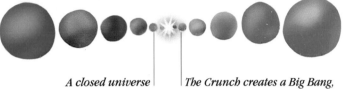

A closed universe collapses, and ends its life in a Big Crunch.

The Crunch creates a Big Bang, and a completely new universe is born on the rebound.

CONSTRUCTIVE SIDE OF BLACK HOLES

Black holes are among the most destructive inhabitants of our Universe: cosmic vortices with such powerful gravity that nothing can escape their pull. Their gravity deforms space itself, creating gravitational wells into which stars and gas fall – to disappear forever. But black holes may have a constructive side. One theory predicts that the matter disappearing down a black hole may "bud" off the bottom of the well to produce another universe.

Baby universe grows

Matter sucked into the black hole "buds off"

Gravitational well of a black hole

A baby universe may bud off from a black hole, fuelled by the enormous energy generated by the black hole's strong gravity.

INFLATION ESSENTIAL FOR SUCCESS

Most of the universes that bubble out of the cosmic foam are doomed to vanish as quickly as they appeared. Only if they manage to undergo inflation will they survive. The green-coloured universe (right) was successful, but it will not necessarily grow to resemble our Universe. With different forces and particles, it may create some very alien objects.

One day, our expanding Universe may collide into another universe like this. No one is sure what the result will be.

WHY THE UNIVERSE IS JUST RIGHT FOR US

Even if other universes exist, ours is special: conditions are just right for us. That is surprising, because the forces of nature are finely balanced: change one slightly, and intelligent life would never have arisen. If gravity were stronger, for instance, stars would burn up too quickly for life to evolve on their planets. According to the "anthropic principle", these forces are chosen at random in each Big Bang. Most universes emerge filled with unstable matter; only in a few are conditions right for life to evolve. The fact that we are here to piece together what happened in the Big Bang, and explore the complexity of the cosmos, may not be coincidence.

Black Holes

THEY ARE THE MOST MYSTERIOUS objects in the cosmos. Ravening monsters lurking in secret places, they are also the most terrifying. They dictate the evolution of mighty galaxies and may even control the ultimate fate of the Universe. But no one has ever seen one.

Black holes are the stuff of science fiction. To astronomers, though, they are as real as the Sun, Moon, and stars. The challenge is to seek them out and discover more about their bizarre properties. Will everything inevitably fall into a black hole? Are they tunnels to other universes? Will they enable us to travel through time?

This section of the book examines the weird world of these bottomless cosmic vortices. From the supernova blasts that create them, through the process of falling into a black hole, to the Big Crunch in which our Universe may die – the ultimate black hole – it explores the mind-boggling and often contradictory behaviour of black holes. Along the way it describes how gravity forms the power of these shadowy occupants of the cosmos, and how black holes warp the very fabric of space. And it looks at some of the hottest areas in black hole research today – mysterious "machos", gravitational waves, baby universes, and wormholes.

Black hole ahead

THEY ARE THE MOST MYSTERIOUS OBJECTS in the cosmos. Ravenous monsters lurking in secret places, they are also the most terrifying. They power the birth pangs of young galaxies, and may control the fate of our whole Universe. They might even be gateways to other universes, quite separate from our own. But despite their bizarre properties no one, yet, has ever seen one. Black holes. The stuff of science fiction. To astronomers, though, they are real – as real as the Sun, the Moon, and the stars – even though they are invisible. This book explores the secret world of black holes, a twilight zone at the very edge of space and time.

A distant quasar – a young, disturbed galaxy – spews jets of hot gas into space from its glaring core. A supermassive black hole is thought to drive the violent activity.

A black hole's powerful gravity plays crazy tricks. Here, it has bent the light of a galaxy lying behind, creating a cosmic mirage. The galaxy appears closer, brighter, and split in two.

Black holes are aptly named. The "Black Hole of Calcutta" was a room in 18th-century India used to hold three prisoners. Once, 46 were crammed in – and 24 died. Just as in its astronomical counterpart, a large amount of matter was concentrated in a small space from which there was no escape.

A galaxy not in line with the black hole looks undistorted. The galaxy itself may contain millions of black holes.

This black hole was created by the explosion of a massive star, a supernova. Were it not for the faint ring of light trapped by its gravity, we would not even suspect the black hole is there.

Seeing the invisible

Black holes have been around since the beginning of time – but we didn't know about them until astronomers developed new ways of looking at the Universe. Instead of using just light, today's astronomers explore space with other wavelengths. Radio waves, infrared, ultraviolet, X-rays, gamma rays – these invisible radiations have brought information of previously unknown and violent events taking place out there. Except for the very smallest, black holes emit no detectable radiation, but their gravity can have a dramatic effect on their surroundings.

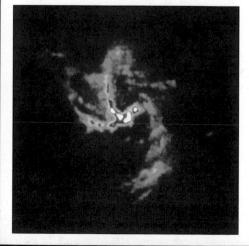

A false-colour image from a radio telescope shows a region 20 light years across at the heart of our Galaxy. It reveals a ring of hot gas circling what is probably a huge black hole.

Fragments of planets orbiting this far from the black hole can escape its clutches

From tiny to supermassive

Black holes come in all sizes. The most common ones, which future spacefarers are bound to encounter, weigh the equivalent of about 10 Suns. These holes are the remains of supernovas – the explosion of massive stars. Then there are supermassive black holes that lurk at the centres of galaxies. Created in the early days of the Universe, they have had almost 15 billion years in which to devour anything that has come too close. The biggest, weighing in at billions of Suns, drove the frenetic activity of quasars when galaxies were young. Now, these supermassive black holes lurk unseen at the heart of many apparently placid galaxies. And at the other extreme, scientists believe there are countless mini black holes the size of atoms. Created when the Universe was born, these holes have been getting steadily smaller.

Lurking among the myriad of stars in our Milky Way Galaxy, there may be millions of black holes

The second of the distorted images of a single galaxy

Debris from a planet orbiting this close will eventually be dragged into the black hole

A dazzling explosion marks the passing of a mini black hole, one that started out as heavy as a mountain but as small as an atom. This type of black hole can lose energy and end its life by exploding in a burst of radiation.

The star that became a black hole

This bleak scene shows the aftermath of a colossal supernova that wrecked a star and destroyed its family of planets. The remains of the star have become a black hole; its planets circle as fragments of debris. If they orbit close to the black hole, gravity will ultimately drag them in. Farther out, it is a different story. Although black holes have a reputation for swallowing everything, their gravitational strength drops off with distance. You can still get reasonably close and stay safe.

Gravity's ultimate triumph

ALL STARS LIVE ON BORROWED TIME. They are born of gravity and, eventually, gravity destroys them. This is spectacularly true in massive stars. A star more than 10 times as heavy as the Sun rips through its nuclear fuel at a prodigious rate – in a few million rather than a few billion years. Once a heavyweight star has exhausted its hydrogen, it has sufficiently high temperatures and pressures to fuse heavier elements. But when it tries to squeeze a core made of iron, all hell breaks loose – leading to one of the most sensational explosions the Universe can provide. A supernova explosion can spawn some bizarre descendants: a neutron star, or even a black hole.

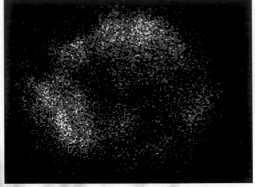

Cassiopeia A is the wreckage of a star that exploded as a supernova about 300 years ago.

Most supernovas are exploding red supergiants hundreds of times bigger than the Sun

A massive star exists in a bloated state for a hundred thousand years before gravity overwhelms it

A supernova explosion may be as brilliant as a billion Suns

Going out with a bang

A few supernovas are the result of one star in a double-star system dumping gas on the other, but most are heavyweight stars dying with a bang. Nuclear reactions have produced a core made of iron – which cannot be used as nuclear fuel. Fusing iron takes in energy rather than giving it out. The result is internal collapse: with the temperature soaring to 50 billion °C (90 billion °F), the core emits a flood of tiny energetic particles, called neutrinos, which rip the star apart.

The star's core attempts to fuse iron. To supply the energy, the star tries to…

…contract its core. The infalling matter bounces off the core and…

…powered by a flood of neutrinos, the star's outer layers are blasted into space

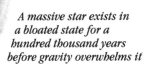

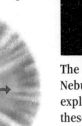

The delicate filaments of the Veil Nebula are the remains of a star explosion 20,000 years ago. From these ashes new stars will arise.

ON THE PULSE

Jocelyn Bell-Burnell and Tony Hewish stand by the radio telescope with which they discovered the first pulsar in 1967. The telescope — a huge field with 2,048 wire aerials suspended on posts — was built to study rapidly flashing sources. By chance, it found regularly repeating pulses from a neutron star.

Superdense lighthouses

A supernova's core collapses in just a few seconds, often producing a pulsar. These are superdense, rotating neutron stars that beam flashes of radiation — like a lighthouse — as they spin. Most pulsars, which are the size of a city such as London, spin about once a second, but the record is 642 times a second!

Pulsars only "pulse" for a million years or so. They lose energy, spin more slowly, and turn into non-pulsing neutron stars

We will never detect many pulsars: their beams are tilted at the wrong angle to sweep past Earth

A pulsar emits two powerful beams of radiation from its poles

If a beam sweeps past us, we detect a pulse

Magnetic pole

Rotation axis

Possible solid core

Magnetic field

Neutron fluid

Solid crust

Beam

The Crab Pulsar is the youngest neutron star we know of. It spins 30 times a second. These images capture it in its "off" (left) and "on" (right) states — "on" when we are in the beam, and "off" when we are not.

FULL OF NEUTRONS

A pulsar is the ultimate in squashed matter. The protons and electrons in the core of the former star have been squeezed to form neutrons — particles with no electrical charge. Standing shoulder to shoulder, the neutrons hold up the pulsar against the force of gravity. This compressed neutron star has a magnetic field about a trillion times more powerful than the Earth's. Its magnetic poles squirt dazzling beams of radiation into space.

SUPERTANKER IN A PINHEAD

The material in a pulsar is much more compressed than in a white dwarf. Gravity squeezes it so tightly that a pinhead of pulsar material would weigh a million tonnes (tons) — twice as much as the world's biggest supertanker.

Black out

Sometimes the relic left after a supernova explosion is too heavy to become a pulsar. If it weighs more than three Suns, not even the superdense neutrons can hold it up against the force of gravity. The object collapses even further to become a black hole.

THE SCALE OF THINGS

A star can take a lot of squeezing. When it becomes a white dwarf, a star like our Sun (1.4 million km/870,000 miles across) packs down to the size of Earth (12,000 km/7,500 miles across). A neutron star, weighing in at 1.5 Suns, is only 25 km (15 miles) across — about the size of Manhattan Island. A black hole may be just a few kilometres in diameter.

A segment of the Sun compared to a white dwarf…

…and part of a white dwarf compared to a neutron star…

…and part of a neutron star compared to a black hole

Discovery of black holes

IN 1970, AMERICAN SCIENTISTS launched a new satellite, *Uhuru*, into orbit. Its job was to track down objects emitting powerful X-rays: energetic radiation that is a sure sign of violent activity in the cosmos. *Uhuru* discovered hundreds of new X-ray sources. In many cases, the source was a compact neutron star ripping gas off a companion star. But Cygnus X-1 was different. At the same position as this X-ray source is a huge, hot blue star, about 30 times more massive than the Sun. This star is being dragged around by an unseen object weighing as much as 10 Suns – well above the limit for neutron stars. Astronomers agree that the invisible object is almost certainly a black hole, the first of several that have now been detected.

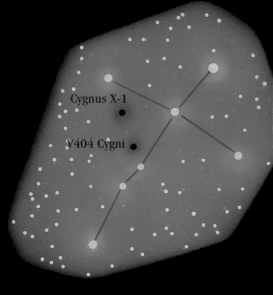

TWO IN ONE
The constellation of Cygnus (the swan) contains two probable black holes. In Cygnus X-1, the hole weighs 10 Suns, while the newly discovered V404 Cygni weighs 12 Suns.

The streamer hits the gas orbiting the black hole, creating a bright "hot spot"

Swallowing a supergiant

Cygnus X-1 and its supergiant companion started life as a double-star system. In close-up now, the pair would be an awesome sight, with the tiny black hole – no more than 30 km (20 miles) across – relentlessly tearing gas from its companion. The gas pours towards the black hole, forming a swirling vortex called an accretion disc. As the gas falls, it travels faster and faster until it is moving close to the speed of light. Friction makes the speeding gas extremely hot, and the accretion disc glares brilliantly. Close to the hole, the gas becomes so hot that it emits X-rays.

This X-ray image of Cygnus X-1 was taken by the satellite *Rosat*. The X-rays are coming from superheated gas circling a black hole about 6,000 light years from Earth.

Uhuru

Launched from Kenya on the 7th anniversary of the country's independence, *Uhuru* is the Swahili word for freedom. It made the first complete survey of the X-ray sky. X-rays cannot penetrate the Earth's atmosphere, and earlier studies had been limited to brief observations during rocket flights. *Uhuru* detected 339 sources of X-ray signals, including Cygnus X-1. The sources of the X-rays are gas heated to a hundred million degrees or higher.

The detectors on *Uhuru* could give only approximate locations for X-ray sources. Today's satellites carry sophisticated telescopes.

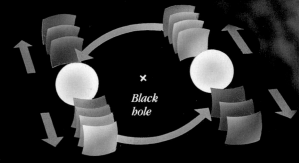

Black hole

As the star approaches us, the light waves bunch together. The star appears to give out light of a shorter (bluer) wavelength

As the star moves away from us, its wave fronts spread out – so we pick up light of a longer (redder) wavelength

HOW TO WEIGH A BLACK HOLE
The black hole's gravity whirls its companion star around – the stronger the gravity, the faster the orbit. If you split the light of the star into its separate colours, you can "weigh" the black hole. The amount the light changes as it approaches and moves away – known as the "Doppler shift" – reveals the speed of the orbit, and hence the mass of the black hole.

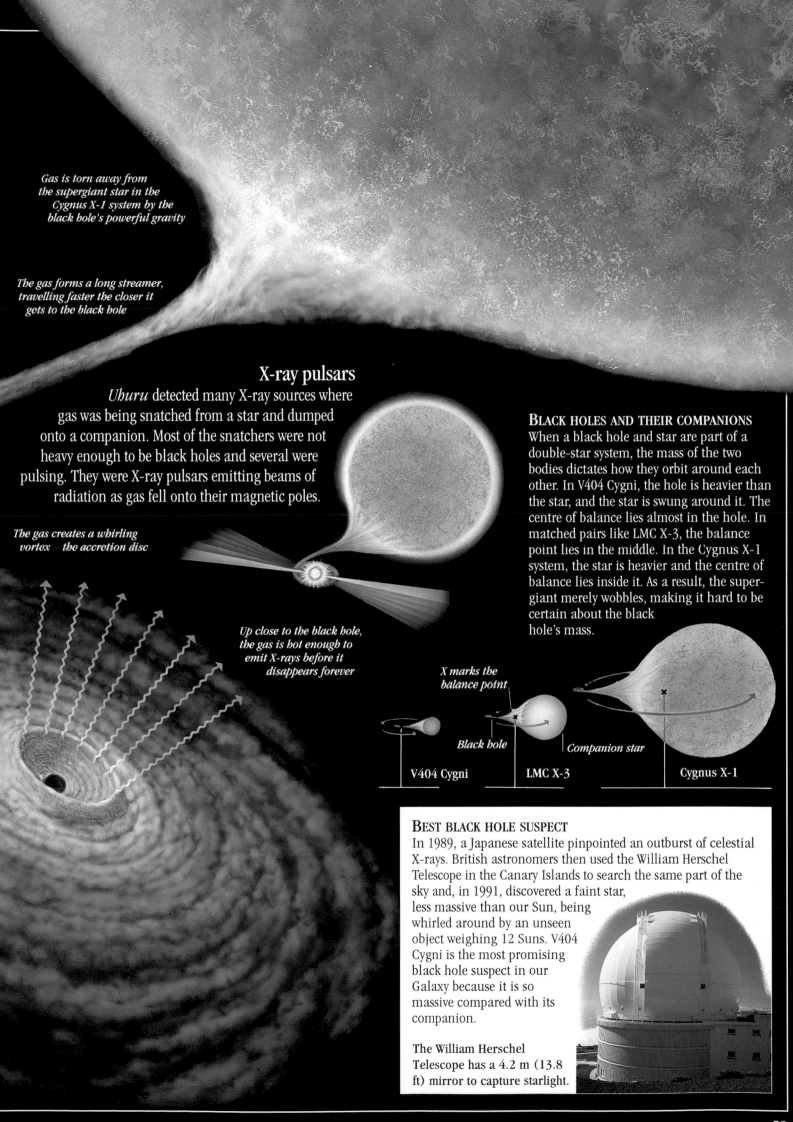

Gas is torn away from the supergiant star in the Cygnus X-1 system by the black hole's powerful gravity

The gas forms a long streamer, travelling faster the closer it gets to the black hole

X-ray pulsars

Uhuru detected many X-ray sources where gas was being snatched from a star and dumped onto a companion. Most of the snatchers were not heavy enough to be black holes and several were pulsing. They were X-ray pulsars emitting beams of radiation as gas fell onto their magnetic poles.

The gas creates a whirling vortex – the accretion disc

Up close to the black hole, the gas is hot enough to emit X-rays before it disappears forever

BLACK HOLES AND THEIR COMPANIONS

When a black hole and star are part of a double-star system, the mass of the two bodies dictates how they orbit around each other. In V404 Cygni, the hole is heavier than the star, and the star is swung around it. The centre of balance lies almost in the hole. In matched pairs like LMC X-3, the balance point lies in the middle. In the Cygnus X-1 system, the star is heavier and the centre of balance lies inside it. As a result, the supergiant merely wobbles, making it hard to be certain about the black hole's mass.

X marks the balance point

Black hole

Companion star

V404 Cygni

LMC X-3

Cygnus X-1

BEST BLACK HOLE SUSPECT

In 1989, a Japanese satellite pinpointed an outburst of celestial X-rays. British astronomers then used the William Herschel Telescope in the Canary Islands to search the same part of the sky and, in 1991, discovered a faint star, less massive than our Sun, being whirled around by an unseen object weighing 12 Suns. V404 Cygni is the most promising black hole suspect in our Galaxy because it is so massive compared with its companion.

The William Herschel Telescope has a 4.2 m (13.8 ft) mirror to capture starlight.

A theory of some gravity

B LACK HOLES APPEAR TO BE SUCH A MODERN CONCEPT that it comes as a surprise to learn that they were predicted more than 200 years ago. In 1784, John Michell, an English clergyman, was pondering whether gravity had an effect on light. He suggested that some stars might be so big that light could never escape from them. A few years later – and apparently by complete coincidence – the French mathematician Pierre Simon de Laplace came to the same conclusion. At the heart of their reasoning was a theory put forward by the great physicist Isaac Newton in 1687. Newton, it is said, watched an apple fall from a tree. The reason it fell, he suggested, was due to a force of attraction called gravity. The more massive (heavier) an object, the greater was its pull of gravity. Hence the apple fell to Earth – and not the other way round.

In his garden at Woolsthorpe Manor, England, Isaac Newton ponders why an apple falls to the ground.

DISTANCE IS IMPORTANT

According to Newton, the farther apart two objects are, the weaker gravity becomes. It decreases as the square of the distance: double the distance between two objects and they feel only a quarter of the gravity. Even on Earth, an object at the top of a very tall tower weighs slightly less than at the bottom, because gravity gets weaker as you move away from the Earth's centre.

At the top of the tower the Earth pulls less strongly on the apple, and so it weighs less

At the bottom of the tower, the Earth and the apple pull on one another more strongly – so the apple weighs more

Forces at work

Newton's great leap of imagination was to realize that every object with mass has a gravitational pull. This means that the forces between an apple and the Earth and the forces that dictate the motions of distant stars are the same. At last, scientists could begin to understand why stars and planets move the way they do, and to predict how they would move in the future.

A powerful Gemini rocket is needed to launch two astronauts into space from Earth

Earth's gravity

KEEPING THE MOON IN PLACE

The Moon orbits the Earth because of the attractive force of gravity between the two. If the Earth were not there, the Moon would fly off in a straight line. But gravity is always pulling it back, and the Moon stays in orbit.

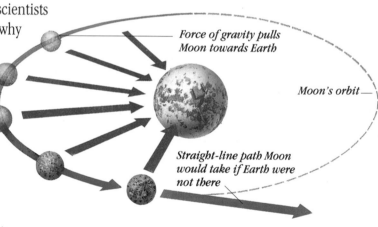

Force of gravity pulls Moon towards Earth

Moon's orbit

Straight-line path Moon would take if Earth were not there

GRAVITY INCREASES WITH MASS

Newton also found that gravity increases with mass. To break the bonds that hold you to a massive body, you must exert a strong opposite force by travelling away quickly. To leave Earth, you need to reach a velocity of 11 km/s (6.8 miles/s) to escape from gravity's pull. Any slower, and you will be pulled back to Earth. The escape velocity for the much less massive Moon is 1.8 km/s (1.1 miles/s).

The low-mass Moon has only one-sixth of the Earth's gravity. A small lunar lander is powerful enough to launch two astronauts from its surface

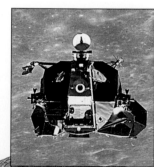

Lunar gravity

Shrinking bodies

Gravity depends on mass and distance, so you can intensify its force by shrinking a body. Imagine squeezing a spherical body of about the size and mass of the Sun. As it gets smaller, the escape velocity rises as the surface and the centre grow closer. To escape, you would need a series of successively more powerful rockets.

A CRUSH ON EARTH

If you could shrink the Earth from its present diameter of 12,756 km (7,926 miles) to the size of this model – a couple of centimetres across – its gravity would become so strong that the escape velocity would rise from 11 km/s (6.8 miles/s) to 300,000 km/s (186,000 miles/s) – the speed of light. The Earth would become a black hole.

The Earth would become a black hole if squeezed enough

ESCAPE VELOCITY

The stronger the gravitational pull of an object, the higher the escape velocity. As a dying star collapses, the escape velocity increases by the square root of the decrease in size – about 1.4 times for a star compressed to half its former diameter.

Most stars eventually collapse to become white dwarfs with an escape velocity of thousands of kilometres or miles a second

Although the object's mass stays the same, the escape velocity rises because the object is smaller and denser

To escape from a spherical body of the same size and mass as our Sun, a launch vehicle would have to travel at 620 km/s (385 miles/s) – more than 2 million km/hr (1 million miles/hr)

Crush the sphere to half its size and escape velocity goes up by 40 per cent even though its mass is the same

Stars as big as solar systems

Instead of thinking about increasing the force of gravity by shrinking stars, John Michell reasoned the other way around. He calculated that a sphere with the same density as the Sun, but 500 times larger in size, would have an escape velocity equal to that of light and so would be invisible. In practice, no star grows this big or this massive.

A star the size of the Solar System would swallow its own light.

Squeeze it to half that size again, and escape velocity rises to 1,240 km/s (770 miles/s)

Crush the sphere to the size of the Earth, and escape velocity rises to 6,500 km/s (4000 miles/s)

When the sphere reaches the size of a neutron star, the escape velocity is over half the speed of light

Black hole

Trapped light rays

Squeezed into a black hole

The natural end product of shrinking a star still further is to create a body with an escape velocity equal to the speed of light. The result is a black hole – a body with such strong gravity that even light cannot escape. Any light rays emitted from the surface would be pulled back.

Enter Albert Einstein

N EWTON'S THEORY OF GRAVITY ruled supreme for 250 years, but it was only a partial explanation of how the Universe works. Scientists were shocked when Albert Einstein came along with his theory of relativity. In fact, Einstein proposed two theories of relativity. The "special theory" of 1905 dealt with matter, energy, and the speed of light. The "general theory" of 1915 concerned gravity. Instead of regarding gravity simply as a force, Einstein looked on it as a distortion of space itself. Where Einstein's predictions differ from Newton's, Einstein's general theory has always proved the more accurate.

Albert Einstein was one of science's most brilliant thinkers, but he was an average student, and began his career as a patents clerk.

Real position of star

Apparent position of star

The huge mass of the Sun distorts the space around it, bending the light rays as they pass

Path of light ray

Einstein's prediction that light is bent by gravity was tested during a solar eclipse.

Einstein said that the gravitational field of an object manifests itself by distorting space. Here space is shown as a rectangular grid, warped by the presence of the Sun

Mercury

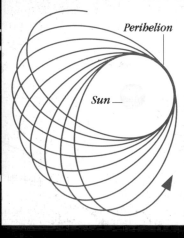

Perihelion

Sun

EINSTEIN'S RIGHT

Mercury, the closest planet to the Sun, has a markedly oval orbit which does not return to the same starting point. The point of closest approach to the Sun (perihelion) is always changing. Newton's theory of gravity cannot explain this unusual orbit, but Einstein's can. As Mercury follows the contours of warped space close to the Sun's large mass, its orbit naturally traces out a complex path in the shape of a rosette.

PASSING THE TEST

Einstein said the Sun's gravity warped space, bending light from stars passing behind it. Astronomers tested his claim in 1919 during a total solar eclipse – the only time stars close to the Sun can be seen. The apparent position of the stars shifted very slightly, exactly as predicted.

Dents in the fabric of space

Einstein thought of empty space as being like a thin rubber sheet. If you place a heavy object, such as a billiard ball, on the sheet, it makes a dent. The Sun, which is the most massive object in the Solar System, warps the space around it, making a small dent, or "gravitational well". Things moving through space follow a curved path when they meet the indentation.

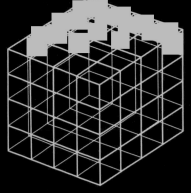

Empty, three-dimensional space can be represented by a cube crossed by straight, regular grid lines

DISTORTIONS IN THREE-DIMENSIONS

To illustrate warped space, we usually draw space as having two dimensions – like the main image on this page. In reality, space is three-dimensional, and the cube on the left is how space would look without any objects in it. A massive object causes distortions, bending the grid lines that map space (below). The natural path of objects through space is not a straight line, but a curved one as they follow the humps and hollows, and "roll" towards more massive objects.

Radio signals to and from the Viking Lander on Mars are delayed by the curvature of space near the Sun – proving Einstein's theory to an accuracy of 0.001 per cent.

Put a massive object into space, and the regular three-dimensional structure becomes distorted

Mars

Venus

According to Einstein, the Sun warps the space around it. The planets whiz around like marbles in a basin, and cannot escape

Radio signals to and from Mars

GENERAL RELATIVITY IN ACTION

On Earth, we notice the effects of living in the Sun's "gravitational well". Light from distant stars is bent and radio signals from space are delayed. The difference between Einstein's and Newton's theory is hard to detect in the Sun's weak gravitational field, but it is much greater near very small, dense bodies – such as a neutron star or a black hole.

NAVIGATING BY EINSTEIN

An ocean-going yacht relies on radio signals from satellites to fix its precise position. The satellites must be programmed according to Einstein's theory of general relativity. If you used Newton's theory, the position would be adrift by 1 km (0.8 miles) every two hours.

Naked singularities

SCIENTISTS INVESTIGATING BLACK HOLES became aware of an alarming possibility in the late 1960s. When a star collapses into a black hole, an event horizon forms and hides the singularity. But in certain situations, a black hole might form without an event horizon. Then it would be possible to see the singularity – and perhaps even to fly to it and away again. But singularities are places of infinite density, where the laws of physics break down and *anything* is possible. And without event horizons, there is nothing to protect the Universe around them: cosmic anarchy would rule. "Naked singularities" could be an irresistible target for fearless future explorers.

A stationary body shrinks to a point

A spinning object shrinks to a ring

A POINT OR A RING?

A singularity is gravity's final triumph – the squeezing of matter to infinite density. If the star or object being compressed is not spinning, gravity shrinks the matter symmetrically. The resulting singularity is an infinitely small point (*left*). If a spinning object is squeezed, the forces of rotation make it bulge into a doughnut shape. This shrinks, and the resulting singularity is an infinitesimally thin ring (*right*).

THE COSMIC CENSOR

British mathematician Roger Penrose proved in 1965 that every black hole contains a singularity. But he was so shocked by the idea of a *naked* singularity that he proposed a "cosmic censor" who would ensure that singularities are decently clothed with an event horizon. That way, the singularity stays cut off from our Universe. But Penrose has not proved that the cosmic censor exists, and other mathematicians believe that naked singularities can exist, even if only briefly.

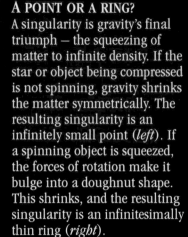

Roger Penrose believes a "cosmic censor" forbids naked singularities.

Journey into the unknown

A spacecraft gingerly approaches a naked singularity. Formed by the collapse of a spinning star, the singularity takes the shape of a glowing ring. Inside and outside the ring, space is normal. The spacecraft can probe the singularity without being dragged in.

Electric forces can make your hair defy gravity…

…while rapid spin can hurl you outward

How to make a naked singularity

The trick is to overcome the forces of gravity that would otherwise create an event horizon. Two forces can achieve this: spin and electric charge. If a body collapsing to become a black hole is spinning very fast or has a strong electric field, the opposing force creates an inner event horizon. Increasing the spin or charge will bring the inner and outer event horizons closer together. If there is enough spin or charge, the two horizons merge and disappear completely, leaving the singularity exposed. In the real Universe, a collapsing star cannot build up enough electric charge to counteract gravity, but a very rapidly spinning star might end up as a naked singularity.

A spinning black hole has an inner and outer event horizon, with a one-way zone between the two where things can only move inward.

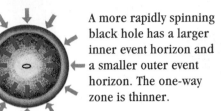

A more rapidly spinning black hole has a larger inner event horizon and a smaller outer event horizon. The one-way zone is thinner.

If the hole spins fast enough, the two horizons may merge. The one-way zone disappears, and the singularity becomes visible – and accessible.

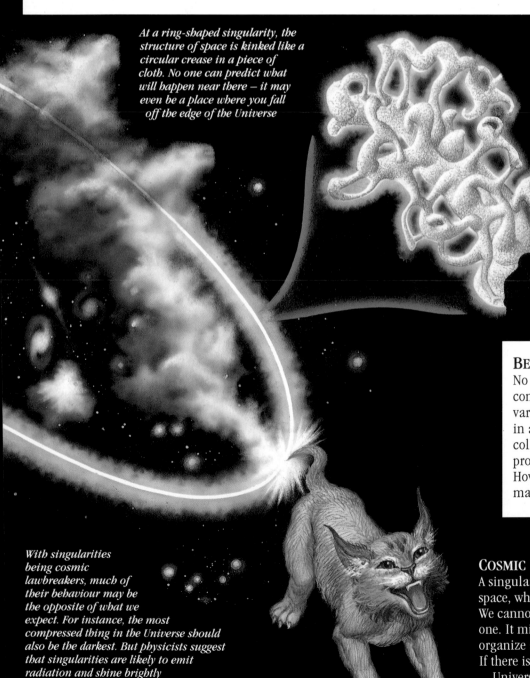

At a ring-shaped singularity, the structure of space is kinked like a circular crease in a piece of cloth. No one can predict what will happen near there – it may even be a place where you fall off the edge of the Universe

Cosmic soapsuds

A ring-shaped singularity is not quite an infinitesimally thin line. Magnified a billion trillion trillion times, we would see the structure of space in its vicinity distorted into a "quantum foam", rather like soapsuds. Space here has no definite shape – only a set of different probable shapes.

With singularities being cosmic lawbreakers, much of their behaviour may be the opposite of what we expect. For instance, the most compressed thing in the Universe should also be the darkest. But physicists suggest that singularities are likely to emit radiation and shine brightly

BEATING THE COSMIC CENSOR

No one has ever seen a naked singularity, but computer simulations suggest they can form in various ways, especially when matter collapses in a very asymmetrical manner. If a long rod collapses under gravity, the simulations produce a thin, elongated naked singularity. However, it lasts only briefly before the whole mass cloaks itself in an event horizon.

COSMIC LAWBREAKERS

A singularity forms an edge or boundary to space, where the laws of physics break down. We cannot predict what will happen near one. It might, for example, spontaneously organize a gas cloud into a huge alien cat. If there is just one naked singularity in the Universe it could cause unpredictable chaos everywhere, even on Earth.

Falling in

BLACK HOLES ARE SO RARE that the risk of getting sucked into one is virtually zero. But what would happen if you did fall into a black hole? On the next four pages, we follow the fate of a future astronaut as she launches herself into a massive black hole (like those that may lurk in the centre of the Milky Way and other galaxies). However, things are seldom simple. Einstein's theory of general relativity reveals that the astronaut's experiences are different from what her anxious crew members – watching from the spacecraft – see her going through. It's all due to the fact that, close to a black hole, both space and time get up to amazing tricks.

Taking the plunge

Watched by her colleagues on the spacecraft, the astronaut sets off, feet-first. The spacecraft is parked at a safe distance, outside the last stable orbit. Aware that both space and time are supposed to be affected by black holes, the crew members monitor the brave astronaut's wristwatch – and also keep tabs on the light coming from their colleague and the distortion of space in her vicinity. To begin with, everything seems normal as she lets the hole's gravity pull her directly downward. Then she starts to plunge towards the hole…

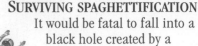

SURVIVING SPAGHETTIFICATION
It would be fatal to fall into a black hole created by a dying star – one with a mass a few times that of the Sun. It warps space so severely that the astronaut falls down a very steep gravitational well. She would feel a much stronger pull on her feet than head. As she got closer to the hole, she would be stretched ever longer and thinner. Eventually, this "spaghettification" would tear her apart.

Spaghettification at the event horizon of a small black hole is equivalent to hanging from the Eiffel Tower with the population of Paris dangling from your feet

MASSIVE MEANS GENTLE
A massive black hole has a much shallower gravitational slope. If the astronaut chose a black hole of 10 million solar masses, she would feel only slight spaghettification forces. They would not be enough to kill.

Light waves coming from the astronaut are normal

Far away from the black hole, space is not distorted

The astronaut's watch and the spacecraft's clock read the same time

1 STARTING OUT
For the first few minutes of the astronaut's journey towards the black hole, nothing appears out of the ordinary. Her wristwatch – viewed by the crew members through a telescope – keeps the same time as the clock on the spacecraft's instrument panel; space in the vicinity (represented by the regular grid at left) is undistorted; and light coming from the astronaut is perfectly normal.

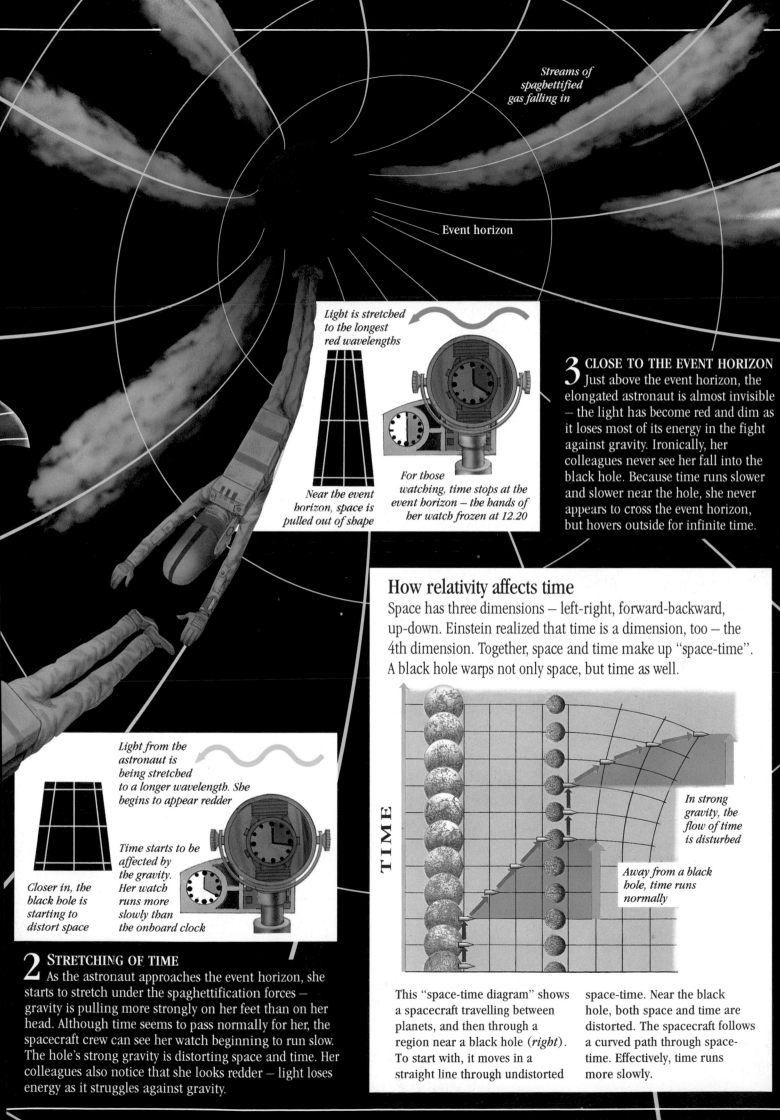

Streams of
spaghettified
gas falling in

Event horizon

*Light is stretched
to the longest
red wavelengths*

3 CLOSE TO THE EVENT HORIZON

Just above the event horizon, the elongated astronaut is almost invisible – the light has become red and dim as it loses most of its energy in the fight against gravity. Ironically, her colleagues never see her fall into the black hole. Because time runs slower and slower near the hole, she never appears to cross the event horizon, but hovers outside for infinite time.

*Near the event
horizon, space is
pulled out of shape*

*For those
watching, time stops at the
event horizon – the hands of
her watch frozen at 12.20*

How relativity affects time

Space has three dimensions – left-right, forward-backward, up-down. Einstein realized that time is a dimension, too – the 4th dimension. Together, space and time make up "space-time". A black hole warps not only space, but time as well.

*Light from the
astronaut is
being stretched
to a longer wavelength. She
begins to appear redder*

*Time starts to be
affected by
the gravity.
Her watch
runs more
slowly than
the onboard clock*

*Closer in, the
black hole is
starting to
distort space*

TIME

*In strong
gravity, the
flow of time
is disturbed*

*Away from a black
hole, time runs
normally*

2 STRETCHING OF TIME

As the astronaut approaches the event horizon, she starts to stretch under the spaghettification forces – gravity is pulling more strongly on her feet than on her head. Although time seems to pass normally for her, the spacecraft crew can see her watch beginning to run slow. The hole's strong gravity is distorting space and time. Her colleagues also notice that she looks redder – light loses energy as it struggles against gravity.

This "space-time diagram" shows a spacecraft travelling between planets, and then through a region near a black hole (*right*). To start with, it moves in a straight line through undistorted space-time. Near the black hole, both space and time are distorted. The spacecraft follows a curved path through space-time. Effectively, time runs more slowly.

71

Through the black hole

THE INTREPID ASTRONAUT feels herself plunging ever faster towards the black hole, unaware that her colleagues watching from the spacecraft see her frozen in time above the event horizon. She has more important things on her mind – like the huge black hole that is looming ahead. There is no escape now. But as she crosses the event horizon, the dark void is suddenly replaced by a dizzying array of fantastic views. Space-time inside the hole is so warped that it allows glimpses of other universes. If the astronaut can carefully navigate her way through the black hole, she may be able to reach another universe.

No turning back: just above the event horizon, the astronaut sees the black hole encircled by a brilliant ring of trapped, orbiting light.

1 CHANGING VIEW

As the astronaut plunges through the black hole, the view through her helmet visor constantly changes. She sees several universes, as if through windows nested inside one another. They may have different stars and dimensions – and even unimaginable kinds of life.

Bridge to another universe

Einstein and his colleague Nathan Rosen suggested that the "throat" of the black hole may open out into a mirror-image throat connected to another universe. In theory, the astronaut should be able to use this Einstein-Rosen bridge to cross to this other universe, but there are considerable dangers ahead. If the black hole is not big enough, she will be pulled apart by the spaghettification forces. If the hole is not spinning, there will be no way she can avoid hitting the infinitely dense singularity at the centre, where she will be killed. A spinning black hole with its ring-shaped singularity could provide the astronaut with a safe path. But she must navigate her way towards the singularity with great care.

Outer event horizon

One-way region – in

Inner event horizon

Polar route

Equatorial route

To survive, you must choose your black hole carefully. It must be big, with a gradual gravitational slope. It must also spin to provide a safe way through.

Navigation is everything. If the astronaut comes in along the black hole's equator, she will hit the singularity. To get through, she must approach from one of the poles

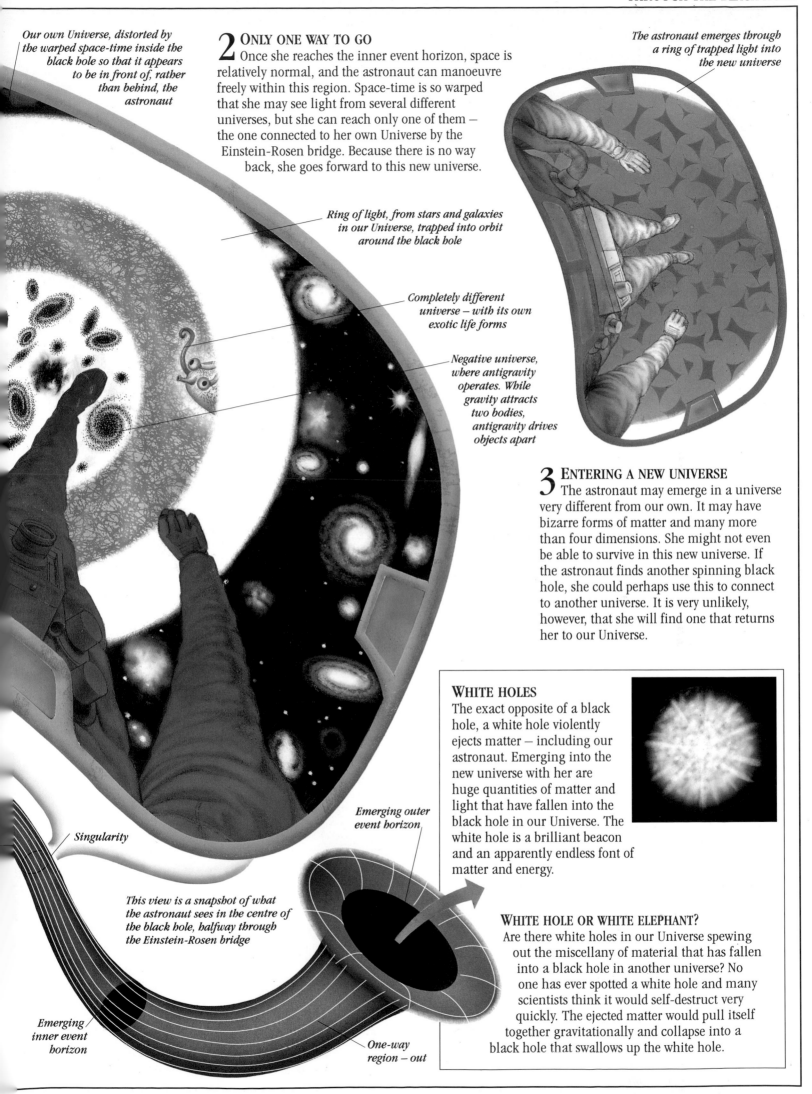

Our own Universe, distorted by the warped space-time inside the black hole so that it appears to be in front of, rather than behind, the astronaut

2 ONLY ONE WAY TO GO

Once she reaches the inner event horizon, space is relatively normal, and the astronaut can manoeuvre freely within this region. Space-time is so warped that she may see light from several different universes, but she can reach only one of them – the one connected to her own Universe by the Einstein-Rosen bridge. Because there is no way back, she goes forward to this new universe.

The astronaut emerges through a ring of trapped light into the new universe

Ring of light, from stars and galaxies in our Universe, trapped into orbit around the black hole

Completely different universe – with its own exotic life forms

Negative universe, where antigravity operates. While gravity attracts two bodies, antigravity drives objects apart

3 ENTERING A NEW UNIVERSE

The astronaut may emerge in a universe very different from our own. It may have bizarre forms of matter and many more than four dimensions. She might not even be able to survive in this new universe. If the astronaut finds another spinning black hole, she could perhaps use this to connect to another universe. It is very unlikely, however, that she will find one that returns her to our Universe.

WHITE HOLES

The exact opposite of a black hole, a white hole violently ejects matter – including our astronaut. Emerging into the new universe with her are huge quantities of matter and light that have fallen into the black hole in our Universe. The white hole is a brilliant beacon and an apparently endless font of matter and energy.

Singularity

This view is a snapshot of what the astronaut sees in the centre of the black hole, halfway through the Einstein-Rosen bridge

Emerging outer event horizon

Emerging inner event horizon

One-way region – out

WHITE HOLE OR WHITE ELEPHANT?

Are there white holes in our Universe spewing out the miscellany of material that has fallen into a black hole in another universe? No one has ever spotted a white hole and many scientists think it would self-destruct very quickly. The ejected matter would pull itself together gravitationally and collapse into a black hole that swallows up the white hole.

Wormholes

BLACK HOLES ARE A PERILOUS WAY TO TRAVEL. Apart from the dangers of spaghettification and collisions with singularities, the tunnel that connects a black hole to another universe stays open only briefly and then collapses. But there may be an alternative, although at the moment it exists only in theory. One day, scientists may be able to turn off the fury of a black hole using antigravity – the opposite of gravity – to create a wormhole. A wormhole has two mouths, connected by a tunnel through curved space. Unlike the event horizon of a black hole, the mouth of a wormhole allows two-way traffic: you can enter and leave. And a wormhole also has the great advantage that it can connect different parts of our own Universe, providing a safe shortcut between two distant places.

BRIEF OPENINGS
A black hole provides an unstable route between our Universe and another. After a black hole forms (*left*), it briefly connects to another universe (*centre*), but the tunnel inevitably collapses (*right*). It may even close prematurely if it is disturbed, for example, by an astronaut trying to travel through.

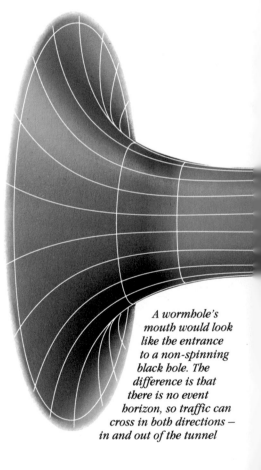

A wormhole's mouth would look like the entrance to a non-spinning black hole. The difference is that there is no event horizon, so traffic can cross in both directions – in and out of the tunnel

One small step into a wormhole
It's the 25th century. At the Kennedy Space Center, Cape Canaveral, a NASA scientist is preparing to go to work. But he won't be using a rocket. No one has for centuries – which is why NASA's armada of launch vehicles sits gently rusting away on the tarmac, a memorial to the quaint, bygone days of rocketry. Instead, he kits himself out in his spacesuit – and enters the waiting mouth of the specially constructed Kennedy Wormhole, which is lined with antigravity material. This "one small step for a man" truly constitutes a giant leap. Stepping into the entrance, the scientist emerges in another world.

Making your own wormhole
It is one thing to keep an existing wormhole open, but there may not always be one to take you where you want to go. The answer is to create one. Make a hollow in space and then gently curve space until your destination is close to the base of the hollow. Make a small hole in the base of the hollow, and another next to your destination. Glue the edges of the holes together. You have made your own personal wormhole, and are free to travel the Universe.

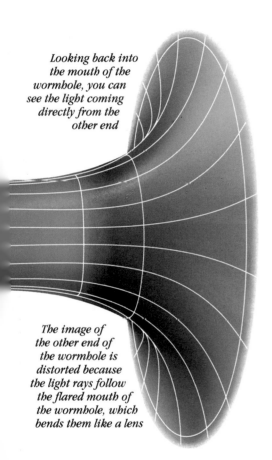

HOLDING A WORMHOLE OPEN WITH ANTIGRAVITY

The tunnel formed between the two mouths of a wormhole is stable: it will not pinch off. But how do we ensure that the tunnel remains open? The trick, according to Kip Thorne, is to reinforce the walls of the tunnel with some sort of exotic material that pushes the wormhole's walls apart. Instead of having gravity, this material must exert antigravity, which forces everything away from it. Thorne believes that, one day, an extremely advanced society will develop the know-how to make an antigravity material.

Created on a car journey

Kip Thorne, an American physicist, was the first person to suggest, in 1985, that wormholes might be used for space travel. Asked by astronomer Carl Sagan to help with his novel *Contact*, Thorne solved the problem on a long car journey. Sagan planned to transport his heroine to the star Vega – 26 light years away – via a black hole. Halfway along Interstate 5, Thorne realized that the only safe way was by wormhole.

Kip Thorne invented the wormhole, but it will take a much more advanced society than ours to build one.

Looking back into the mouth of the wormhole, you can see the light coming directly from the other end

The image of the other end of the wormhole is distorted because the light rays follow the flared mouth of the wormhole, which bends them like a lens

STRAIGHT-LINE SHORTCUT

A wormhole can provide a swift, straight-line route between two parts of our Universe, no matter how far apart they are. Since space can be curved, or folded, the length of the wormhole can stay the same, whether connecting distant or close parts of the Universe. Going by wormhole is far quicker than travelling at the speed of light to very distant parts of the Universe.

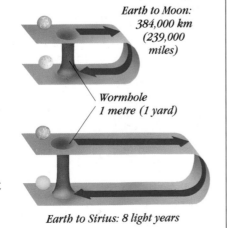

Earth to Moon: 384,000 km (239,000 miles)

Wormhole 1 metre (1 yard)

Earth to Sirius: 8 light years

One giant leap across space

The NASA scientist emerges from the wormhole into the Moon base. It has taken him no time at all to cross the 384,000 km (239,000 miles) that separate the Moon from the Earth – a journey that took the Apollo astronauts three days. Through the mouth of the wormhole, you can see the image of the rusty rockets back on Earth. That's because light also travels through the wormhole, although it is distorted by the antigravity material pushing the light beams apart. Look at the picture of the Kennedy Space Center on the opposite spread, and you'll see the corresponding image of the Moon base through the other wormhole mouth.

Time travel

ONE DAY BLACK HOLES MAY GIVE US a means of travelling through the exotic reaches of space – and possibly into other universes. They may even provide the key to making a journey through time. To be a time traveller, you need a "tamed" black hole: a wormhole. The idea of time travel through a wormhole does not seem so far-fetched when you consider that wormholes are shortcuts to very distant places in curved space (see p. 74). They take you to a remote location in almost no time at all, so it is like travelling faster than the speed of light. And Einstein's special theory of relativity says that if something is able to travel faster than light, it will move backwards through time. So wormholes may be the gateways into the past. Follow the scientist's weird experiences as he creates a time machine using a wormhole.

Bill and Ted's Excellent Adventure: two students about to flunk a history course use a phone-booth time machine to bring historical figures to the present.

Twenty years have passed on Earth, and the scientist is 40

Another 10 years, and the scientist is 50

On a speeding spacecraft, time moves more slowly than on Earth. When she returns, the astronaut twin is aged 35, but the twin who stayed on Earth is 70

2 OUT STEPS THE FUTURE

At age 30, the scientist finds an aged man climbing through the wormhole, followed by a gang of futuristically clad children. He is face-to-face with himself, aged 70.

The twin on the spacecraft speeds away from Earth at 98 per cent of the speed of light

After 5 years have lapsed on the onboard clock, the space twin turns around and speeds back to Earth

Time on Earth is passing. The scientist is now 26

TIME

The twins paradox

We are all travelling into the future as time passes, but Einstein's theory of special relativity can provide a shortcut through time. Start with a pair of twins. While one remains on Earth, her astronaut sister blasts off into space at almost the speed of light. Relativity tells us that the faster an object moves, the slower time on it appears to pass – an effect known as time dilation. When the speeding astronaut returns, she has hardly aged, while her twin on Earth is an old woman. This method cannot, however, take us back into the past.

At the start, the twins are aged 25. Both are living on Earth, and time passes at the same rate for each of them

The scientist is 20 years old when the spacecraft blasts off

Wormhole to the past

Combine the "twins paradox" with a wormhole, and you could create a time machine that allows us to travel both ways in time. Kip Thorne suggests attaching one end of a wormhole to a speeding spacecraft, while the other end stays on Earth. In this example, 50 years pass on Earth before the spacecraft returns. But on the spaceship, only 10 years have elapsed, so the wormhole connects the spacecraft with the Earth as it was 40 years earlier. By stepping onto the spacecraft and through the wormhole, future humans could travel decades back into the past.

GRANDMOTHER PARADOX

A mad scientist, intent on evil deeds, creates a wormhole. Travelling back in time through the wormhole, he finds his grandmother as a young girl – and kills her. But if he killed his grandmother, then she would not have been able to give birth to the scientist's mother. She, in turn, could not have given birth to the scientist. The scientist wouldn't exist – so how could he go back in time and murder his grandmother? Such paradoxes prompt some scientists to declare time travel must be impossible.

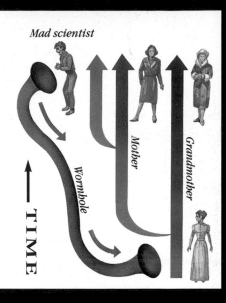

Mad scientist

Wormhole

Mother

Grandmother

TIME

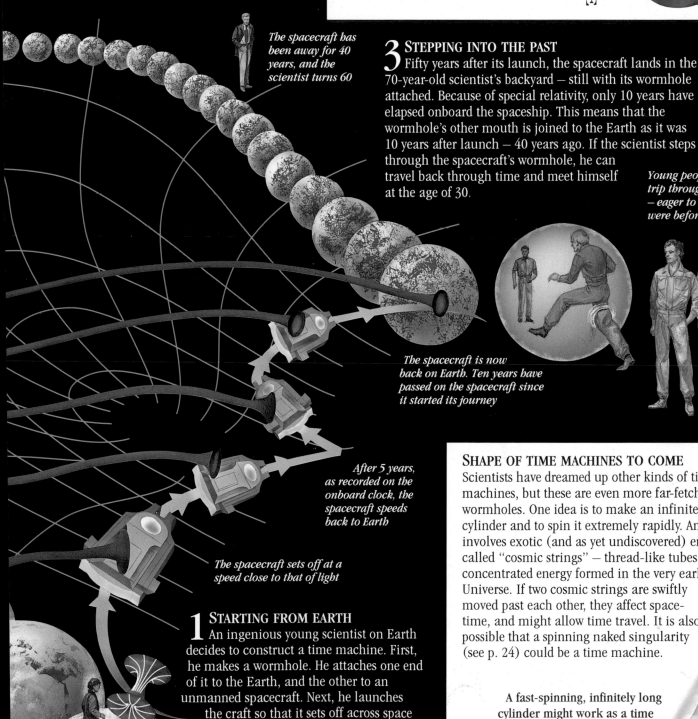

The spacecraft has been away for 40 years, and the scientist turns 60

3 STEPPING INTO THE PAST

Fifty years after its launch, the spacecraft lands in the 70-year-old scientist's backyard – still with its wormhole attached. Because of special relativity, only 10 years have elapsed onboard the spaceship. This means that the wormhole's other mouth is joined to the Earth as it was 10 years after launch – 40 years ago. If the scientist steps through the spacecraft's wormhole, he can travel back through time and meet himself at the age of 30.

Young people queue for a trip through the wormhole – eager to see how things were before they were born

The spacecraft is now back on Earth. Ten years have passed on the spacecraft since it started its journey

After 5 years, as recorded on the onboard clock, the spacecraft speeds back to Earth

The spacecraft sets off at a speed close to that of light

1 STARTING FROM EARTH

An ingenious young scientist on Earth decides to construct a time machine. First, he makes a wormhole. He attaches one end of it to the Earth, and the other to an unmanned spacecraft. Next, he launches the craft so that it sets off across space at a considerable fraction of the speed of light. He has programmed the spaceship to return later on. Now, all he has to do is sit back and wait….

SHAPE OF TIME MACHINES TO COME

Scientists have dreamed up other kinds of time machines, but these are even more far-fetched than wormholes. One idea is to make an infinitely long cylinder and to spin it extremely rapidly. Another involves exotic (and as yet undiscovered) entities called "cosmic strings" – thread-like tubes of concentrated energy formed in the very early Universe. If two cosmic strings are swiftly moved past each other, they affect space-time, and might allow time travel. It is also possible that a spinning naked singularity (see p. 24) could be a time machine.

A fast-spinning, infinitely long cylinder might work as a time machine. But it would need to be made of ultradense matter to stop it from flying apart.

Exploding black holes

BLACK HOLES CAN SHINE BRIGHTLY, shrink in size, and even explode. When British physicist Stephen Hawking made this prediction in 1974, it shook the scientific world. Black holes were regarded as the ultimate sinks of the cosmos: nothing could get out, and holes could only grow bigger as they gained mass by swallowing gas and stars. Hawking's theory was an inspired leap of the imagination that combined general relativity with quantum theory – the physics of the very small. He found that energy is emitted by the gravitational field around a black hole, draining away its energy and mass. This "Hawking radiation" is negligible for most black holes, but very small ones radiate energy at a high rate until they explode violently.

The quantum view

On a very small scale, space has some peculiar properties. A pair of particles can appear out of nothing, created in a burst of energy borrowed from a gravitational field. There is always one ordinary particle, such as an electron, and its antimatter twin, such as a positron. Usually, they collide within a fraction of a second, annihilating each other and releasing the borrowed energy. But close to a black hole, one particle may be pulled inside the event horizon, leaving the other free to escape. To the outside Universe, it seems that a particle of matter has been created.

One particle falls into the hole; its twin escapes. Escaping particles create a glowing halo around the black hole

Close to a black hole, the pairs start to feel the pull of gravity

Particle-antiparticle pairs continually form and annihilate one another

THE AMAZING SHRINKING BLACK HOLE
When a particle escapes from a black hole without repaying its borrowed energy, the hole forfeits this amount of energy from its gravitational field. And as Einstein's equation $E=mc^2$ says, if you lose energy, you lose mass. The black hole becomes lighter in weight and shrinks.

THE PARTICLE AND ITS ANTIPARTICLE TWIN
Atoms – the basic units that make up everything in our Universe – are made of particles called protons, neutrons, and electrons. All subatomic particles like these have antimatter "twins", with opposite properties (including electric charge). A burst of energy can create a particle and its antiparticle: when they meet up again, they annihilate each other in an explosion of equal energy.

Physicists can create particle-antiparticle pairs in particle accelerators. Here a burst of energy produces an electron (green) and its antimatter twin, a positron (red). They spiral in opposite directions.

Near a massive black hole, space curves gently. Most of the particle-antiparticle pairs created here meet up again and annihilate each other

Two pairs have lost their partners

A QUESTION OF TIMING

Stephen Hawking spends his working life studying black holes and the origin of the Universe. Disabled by a crippling disease, Hawking cannot write or speak (he has to store complex concepts in his head). Mental arithmetic led to his prediction that black holes eventually explode, with the most massive holes having the longest lifetime. Hawking suggested that mini black holes born in the Big Bang should be exploding right now.

An assortment of black holes was created by the tremendous forces that existed shortly after the Big Bang that spawned our Universe

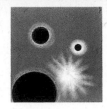

The smallest, weighing a million tonnes (tons) – about the weight of a supertanker – exploded within 10 years

Mini black holes – those weighing a billion tonnes (tons) – should be exploding now, about 15 billion years after the Big Bang

A black hole as heavy as an asteroid will live much longer than the Universe – for more than a million million million years

Hawking's mini black holes have the mass of a mountain but are the size of the nucleus of an atom

Boiling away to destruction

All black holes evaporate, but big ones boil away only very slowly. Their radiation is so dim that it is undetectable. But as the hole gradually gets smaller, the process speeds up, and eventually runs away with itself. As the hole shrinks, so the gravitational well steepens, creating more escaping particles and robbing the black hole of ever more energy and mass. The hole shrinks more and more quickly, fuelling an ever faster rate of evaporation. The surrounding halo becomes brighter and hotter. When its temperature reaches a quadrillion degrees, the black hole destroys itself in an explosion.

In the final stages, the black hole explodes in less than a millionth of a second with the energy of a billion hydrogen bombs

As the hole shrinks, it emits more particles. Its halo appears ever hotter and brighter

WHO LOSES ENERGY FASTEST

The rate at which a black hole shrinks depends on its mass. Curiously, small, low-mass black holes lose energy fastest. What is important is the curvature of space around the black hole. A small black hole has a much steeper gravitational well than a large, high-mass black hole. Just as an astronaut approaching a small hole suffers greater "spaghettification" effects (see p. 70), so the steeper well of a small hole is more effective in splitting a particle from its antiparticle twin.

In the steeply curved space near a small black hole, four pairs have lost their partners

TELLTALE SIGNS

A mini black hole explodes in a burst of gamma rays, the most energetic radiation of all. Astronomers are looking for this telltale burst of radiation, but although many objects in space produce gamma rays, none has been identified as an exploding black hole.

Downtown in the Milky Way

THE UNIVERSE CONTAINS some immensely massive black holes – millions or billions of times heavier than the Sun. They were probably born during the early days of the Universe, when huge balls of gas accumulated and collapsed under their own gravity. Until recently, astronomers thought all of these lay a long way away, but one may live in our own home galaxy, the Milky Way. New telescopes and satellites are revealing unsuspected violence "downtown" in the Galaxy's centre, which is about 25,000 light years from the Sun. An erupting ring of dark clouds, contorted magnetic fields, racing clouds of hot gas, and a peculiar source of radio waves all point to the work of a single culprit: a supermassive black hole lurking in the heart of our own "star city"

The radio telescope at Effelsberg, in Germany, is larger than a football pitch and can be tipped to point to any part of the sky. It has revealed magnetic loops in the Galaxy's centre.

On a clear night you can see the distant stars of our Galaxy as the glowing band of the Milky Way.

Seeing through the smog

From the outskirts of our Galaxy, it is hard to see the "downtown" area because the Milky Way is thick with tiny grains of rock and soot shed by dying stars. But telescopes which can pick up infrared, radio waves, and X-rays can "see" through the smog. They show that the Galaxy has a central "hub" of old stars that date from its birth 14 billion years ago, and reveal a hotbed of activity at its heart.

COBE
The *Cosmic Background Explorer* (*COBE*) satellite was launched in 1989 to find heat radiation from the Big Bang. But it also detected infrared radiation from the central regions of the Milky Way, showing that the stars here are arranged on an oval hub, or "bar".

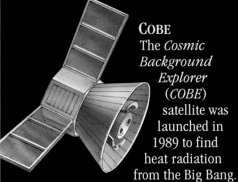

RADIO ACTIVITY IN SAGITTARIUS
The heart of our Galaxy lies deep inside the star clouds of Sagittarius. In the pioneering days of radio astronomy, researchers discovered two strong radio sources here – Sagittarius A and B. We now know these are clouds of hot gas associated with violent activity in the galactic centre.

The old stars in the central hub are cool stars, shining orange or red

Quiet in the suburbs

As galaxies go, the Milky Way is quite a big one. It contains around 200 billion stars, arranged in a spiral pattern 100,000 light years across. The Sun lies in the suburbs in a spiral arm about halfway out from the centre. The arms are rich in gas and dust – the raw materials of stars – so stars are still being born here. By contrast, the stars in the central hub are old and there is little activity there – apart from a tiny energetic core at the very centre.

SMOKE RING
A giant smoke ring of dark clouds, thick with dust and molecules, is rapidly expanding from a titanic explosion several million years ago. The culprit must have been a small, powerful object in the central core.

Black hole at the heart

The central core of our Galaxy – just 10 light years across – is full of weird happenings. There is no absolute proof, but they could be the work of a black hole three million times heavier than the Sun, born during the formation of our Galaxy. Only the powerful gravity of such a beast could explain the hotbed of activity.

Sagittarius B2 is the biggest dark cloud in the downtown area. It contains over 70 different types of molecules, including enough alcohol to fill the Earth with whisky!

The dense scrum in the galactic centre contains young blue stars as well as numerous old red and orange stars

HOT GAS CLOUDS

A ring of hot gas, Sagittarius A, is swirling around several light years from the Galaxy's centre. Its speed shows that the gas is in the grip of a powerful gravitational pull – far stronger than the pull of the stars at the centre. Most likely, the extra pull comes from the gravity of a black hole.

CENTRAL RADIO SOURCE

A very small but intensely powerful radio source marks the Galaxy's exact centre. It is probably an accretion disc of superhot gas surrounding a massive black hole.

Sagittarius A

Infalling gas that missed the black hole could be the raw material for the young hot stars that are shining blue in the centre

Hot gases are rushing out from the core – possibly the result of explosions in the power-packed accretion disc

The gale of gases tears away the outer layers of a red giant star, creating a long tail which makes the star look like a huge comet

Magnetic barrel

MAGNETIC BARREL

A barrel-shaped region of strong magnetic fields surrounds the Galaxy's centre. It includes the contorted band called The Arc – narrow magnetic streamers 150 light years long but just half a light year thick. The Arc's shape indicates that there must be a powerful electric dynamo at the galactic centre. Could it be the work of a spinning black hole?

The Arc

ROSAT

Rosat, an international satellite, was launched in 1990 to detect natural X-rays from space. It has discovered almost 100,000 new objects that emit X-rays, and has pinned down the position of many strange objects, including the Great Annihilator.

Great Annihilator

GREAT ANNIHILATOR

Just 300 light years from the Galaxy's centre, an object is spitting out two beams of anti-matter which annihilate, or destroy, ordinary matter in surrounding space. The beams are probably being generated by an accretion disc surrounding a black hole weighing in at 10 Suns. This is just one of an estimated 100 million black holes in our Galaxy produced by the deaths of massive stars.

THE MOUSE

Radio telescopes reveal isolated patches of magnetism. This one, shaped like a mouse, was caused by a pulsar leaving a magnetic wake as it sped through space.

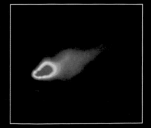

Quasars

WHEN QUASARS WERE DISCOVERED IN 1963, no one realized they were looking at objects that harboured the biggest black holes in the Universe. After all, they look just like faint stars. Astronomers soon worked out that quasars are billions of light years away, and to be visible at that distance, they must be immensely bright. In fact, they are not stars at all, but the glaring hearts of remote galaxies – star cities in such turmoil that the Milky Way's activity looks tame. The only way so much energy can be concentrated into such a small region is by the gravity exerted by a truly massive black hole. The brilliant light is an accretion disc of gas spiralling into the hole. Astronomers can weigh the black hole in a quasar by measuring the speed of orbiting stars or gas: the higher the speed, the heavier the hole. The record is a black hole weighing in at 100 billion Suns – as massive as the entire Milky Way.

Jets of charged particles – mostly electrons – shoot out from the centre of the accretion disc. The jets can be thousands of light years long

Breakneck speeds

This is the heart of a quasar – a glaring accretion disc made up of gas, torn-up stars, and dirty dust whirls at breakneck speed around a supermassive black hole, weighing in at billions of Suns. This activity powers jets that shoot into space at almost the speed of light.

GAS BOWL

A quasar's brilliant light comes from the hot gas at the centre of the accretion disc. The expansion of this gas, together with the forces of gravity and rotation, push the two faces of the disc apart, creating a bowl shape. Powerful magnetic fields speed up atomic particles in the gas and force them away as a pair of jet

ACTIVE FAMILY

Quasars have cousins in the radio galaxies and blazars: all three are often called "active galaxies". In fact, they may be one and the same. What we see depends on the angle at which we are viewing them: whether we are seeing the accretion disc and jet face-on, edge-on, or at an angle to us.

If the accretion disc is angled to us, we see a quasar: we observe the hot core of the disc and the jets are dim

The galaxy M87, imaged here by the *Hubble Space Telescope*, has a jet emerging from the vicinity of a black hole weighing 3 billion Suns.

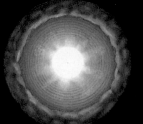

A blazar's brilliant light comes mainly from the jet: it and the accretion disc are pointing straight toward us

In a radio galaxy, the edge of the accretion disc is facing us, and it obscures the hot, bright core. The jets may be observable by a radio telescope

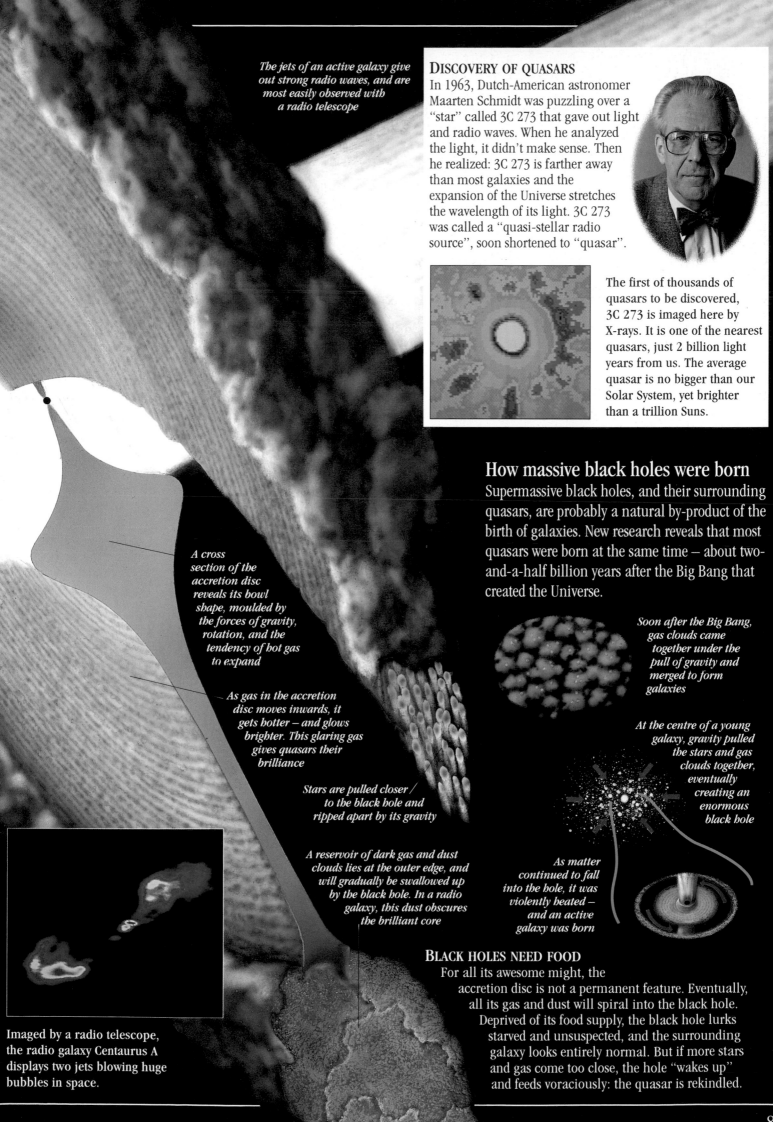

The jets of an active galaxy give out strong radio waves, and are most easily observed with a radio telescope

DISCOVERY OF QUASARS

In 1963, Dutch-American astronomer Maarten Schmidt was puzzling over a "star" called 3C 273 that gave out light and radio waves. When he analyzed the light, it didn't make sense. Then he realized: 3C 273 is farther away than most galaxies and the expansion of the Universe stretches the wavelength of its light. 3C 273 was called a "quasi-stellar radio source", soon shortened to "quasar".

The first of thousands of quasars to be discovered, 3C 273 is imaged here by X-rays. It is one of the nearest quasars, just 2 billion light years from us. The average quasar is no bigger than our Solar System, yet brighter than a trillion Suns.

How massive black holes were born

Supermassive black holes, and their surrounding quasars, are probably a natural by-product of the birth of galaxies. New research reveals that most quasars were born at the same time – about two-and-a-half billion years after the Big Bang that created the Universe.

Soon after the Big Bang, gas clouds came together under the pull of gravity and merged to form galaxies

A cross section of the accretion disc reveals its bowl shape, moulded by the forces of gravity, rotation, and the tendency of hot gas to expand

As gas in the accretion disc moves inwards, it gets hotter – and glows brighter. This glaring gas gives quasars their brilliance

At the centre of a young galaxy, gravity pulled the stars and gas clouds together, eventually creating an enormous black hole

Stars are pulled closer to the black hole and ripped apart by its gravity

A reservoir of dark gas and dust clouds lies at the outer edge, and will gradually be swallowed up by the black hole. In a radio galaxy, this dust obscures the brilliant core

As matter continued to fall into the hole, it was violently heated – and an active galaxy was born

BLACK HOLES NEED FOOD

For all its awesome might, the accretion disc is not a permanent feature. Eventually, all its gas and dust will spiral into the black hole. Deprived of its food supply, the black hole lurks starved and unsuspected, and the surrounding galaxy looks entirely normal. But if more stars and gas come too close, the hole "wakes up" and feeds voraciously: the quasar is rekindled.

Imaged by a radio telescope, the radio galaxy Centaurus A displays two jets blowing huge bubbles in space.

Mirages and ripples

WHEN IT COMES TO TRACKING DOWN BLACK HOLES, astronomers are very resourceful. To find something so dark, they have to seek out telltale clues. Streams of snatched hot gas from an orbiting companion star, disruption in the hearts of galaxies and quasars, bursts of gamma rays – all these may be signs of a black hole at work. Recently, astronomers have discovered two new clues. Both rely on gravity and the effects predicted by Einstein. The first involves seeking out cosmic mirages. When light from a distant object passes close to a region of strong gravity, it is bent or distorted, giving rise to some bizarre optical effects. The second method entails detecting "ripples in space" – gravitational waves – created by the movement of massive objects.

Cosmic mirages

Einstein's theory of relativity says that when light passes close to a massive object such as the Sun, it is bent (see p. 62). A black hole has such strong gravity that it deflects and focuses light from a distant star so that it appears brighter than normal.

Gravitational waves may be caused by two massive bodies – black holes or neutron stars – in orbit about each other. They may also be produced by a supernova explosion or the merger of two neutron stars

The waves – "ripples in space" – spread out from their source at the speed of light

Light from a star in the Large Magellanic Cloud sets out on a journey of 170,000 light years towards the Earth

The light rays enter the galactic halo – a zone of scattered old stars surrounding the Milky Way

In the halo, the starlight passes near a black hole, where the warped space focuses the light rays

GALACTIC MIRAGES
A black hole works like a small lens, and its main effect is to make a star behind it look brighter. The distortion of space close to a galaxy, on the other hand, acts like a giant lens, spreading the light from a distant object so that there appear to be several objects instead of one. Here, a galaxy 400 million light years away deflects and splits light from a quasar 8 billion light years behind it, creating four quasar images around the central galaxy.

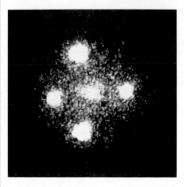

Four mirages of the quasar 2237 + 0305, popularly known as the Einstein Cross, captured by the Hubble Space Telescope.

Machos at work

The warped space near a black hole works like a lens in a telescope, bending and focusing the light rays from a distant star so that it temporarily appears brighter. Astronomers have observed this effect in stars belonging to the Large Magellanic Cloud, a small galaxy orbiting the Milky Way. They believe that the culprits are black holes or neutron stars living in the outer regions, or "halo", of our Galaxy. These have been nicknamed MACHOs — MAssive Compact Halo Objects.

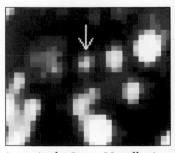

A star in the Large Magellanic Cloud at its normal brightness.

Ripples in space

If both members of a double-star system are supermassive giants that end their days exploding as supernovas, the end result may be a double black hole system. Like two circling speedboats, the black holes orbit around each other creating massive wakes of gravitational waves that spread, like ripples, through space.

Bouncing laser beams should be able to detect microscopic changes in the distance between two mirrors several kilometres apart as a gravitational wave passes through. This is a small prototype to test the laser systems.

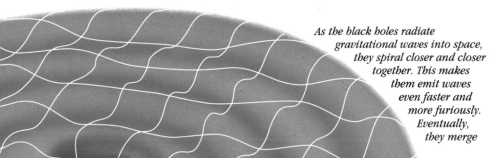

As the black holes radiate gravitational waves into space, they spiral closer and closer together. This makes them emit waves even faster and more furiously. Eventually, they merge

WAVES THAT STRETCH AND SHRINK

Gravitational waves are shudders in the fabric of space, caused by the movement of massive bodies. Einstein predicted that the waves should exist, but no one yet has found them. In theory, they should shrink or stretch any object they pass through. But the effects are very small. A gravitational wave passing through an iron bar 1 metre (39 inches) long would change its length by the diameter of the nucleus of an atom. Detectors need to be extremely sensitive.

Gravitational waves cause distortions in the shape of space, just as waves ripple the surface of the sea

The most solid of objects are distorted when a gravitational wave passes through them. But the amount of stretching or compression is tiny

At the Laser Interferometer Gravitational Wave Observatory in California, laser beams travelling through tunnels 4 km (2.5 miles) long should register the tiny changes produced by gravitational waves

BRIEF BRIGHTENING

In 1993, astronomers found a star that suddenly brightened in the Large Magellanic Cloud. After a month, it faded again. The best explanation is that a black hole passed in front and briefly focused the star's light our way. The hole weighed only one-tenth as much as the Sun, and lay 20,000 light years away.

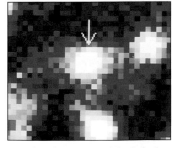

Star brightens as a black hole passes in front, focusing its light.

An optical telescope detects the brightening of a star in the Large Magellanic Cloud

Biggest black hole

A VERY DARING IDEA HAS EMERGED IN RECENT YEARS: we may be living within a black hole! Some scientists have suggested that the entire Universe is a huge black hole, of a rather different kind. It is not surrounded by an event horizon, but curves back on itself like the surface of a balloon. The result is the same: you cannot escape. The Universe has no central singularity. Instead, it had a singularity in the past, the Big Bang in which the Universe began – and it may collapse back into a singularity in the future, the Big Crunch. The theory links black holes and universes so closely that it predicts a black hole can actually create a new universe.

TIME →

The Universe keeps expanding, pushing the galaxies away from each other as the space between them is increased

As time passes and the Universe cools down and expands, quasar activity dies down, leaving normal galaxies

A couple of billion years after the Big Bang, the Universe is full of quasars

THE BEGINNING
No one knows what caused the Big Bang: it may have been a fluctuation out of literally nothing. Fractions of a second afterwards, the temperature and density in the cosmic fireball were almost infinite. In the inferno, dozens of strange particles were created which, as the Universe cooled and expanded, formed the nuclei of the first atoms. Around 2 billion years later, these clumped together to make quasars – violent young galaxies with black holes in their hearts. Meanwhile, the Universe continued its expansion.

The Universe today, 15 billion years after the Big Bang, has expanded until it consists of widely separated galaxies

When the Universe is about 50 million times its present age, expansion will stop – if there is enough matter to counteract the momentum created by the Big Bang

Born to a black hole
Far from being merely cosmic sinks, black holes may give birth to other universes. "Baby" universes may "bud" off black holes to grow as universes in completely different dimensions with totally different properties. Depending on the amount of matter in each universe, they will be of different sizes but, like ours, will expand and contract, and produce still more universes along the way.

Universe 1   Universe 1

Universe 2

TIME →

The remains of a supernova in our Universe (universe 1) starts to collapse and form a black hole in the usual way

A baby universe (2) buds off from the black hole. It detaches into a different dimension and becomes independent. This is the Big Bang for universe 2

Universe 2 starts to expand. Black holes that form inside it will create sites where other universes can bud off

From big bang to big crunch

If our Universe is a black hole, then it has a finite, and predictable, lifetime. At the Big Bang, the Universe starts expanding – shown here (not to scale) as a series of inflating balloons. The galaxies and other constituents of the Universe lie on the skin of the balloon, which represents space and carries the galaxies apart as it swells. The history of the Universe is shown on successive strips of the balloons. The Universe expands until it reaches its maximum size; then gravity wins over the momentum from the Big Bang. The Universe begins to contract. The galaxies move closer together and collapse into another singularity – the Big Crunch.

DARK MATTER APPLIES THE GRAVITATIONAL BRAKES

The fate of the Universe depends crucially on how much matter it contains. Too little, and there will not be enough to exert the gravitational pull needed to "brake" the growth of the Universe; it will expand forever. With sufficient matter, it will recollapse. Adding up all the visible matter in the Universe gives only 10 per cent of the mass needed to apply the brakes. But astronomers have evidence that the Universe contains huge quantities of

"dark matter". Perhaps 90 per cent of it consists of this invisible matter, which could comprise exotic subatomic particles or even vast numbers of black holes.

The NGC 2300 cluster of galaxies is embedded in a gas cloud (coloured magenta) weighing 500 billion Suns. The gravity from a vast amount of dark matter must be holding the gas cloud together.

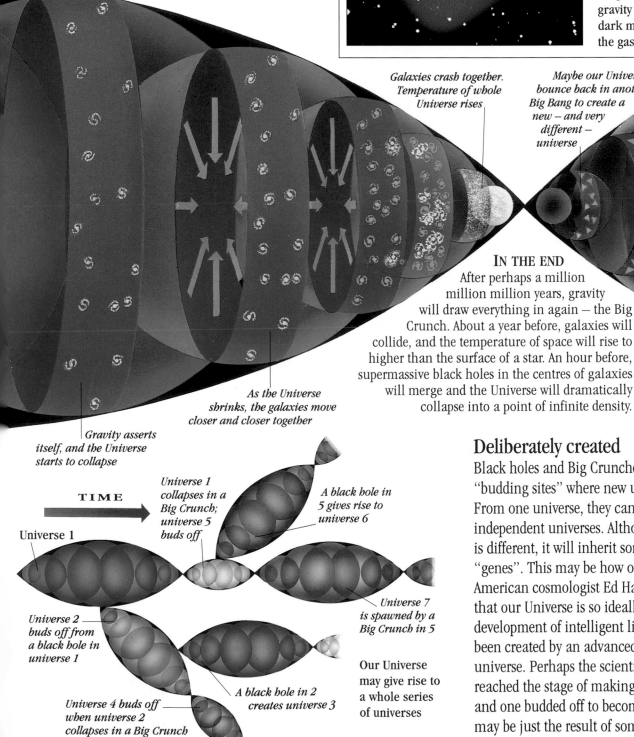

Galaxies crash together. Temperature of whole Universe rises

Maybe our Universe will bounce back in another Big Bang to create a new – and very different – universe

As the Universe shrinks, the galaxies move closer and closer together

IN THE END

After perhaps a million million million years, gravity will draw everything in again – the Big Crunch. About a year before, galaxies will collide, and the temperature of space will rise to higher than the surface of a star. An hour before, supermassive black holes in the centres of galaxies will merge and the Universe will dramatically collapse into a point of infinite density.

The Universe may continually oscillate between Big Bangs and Big Crunches

Gravity asserts itself, and the Universe starts to collapse

TIME

Universe 1

Universe 1 collapses in a Big Crunch; universe 5 buds off

A black hole in 5 gives rise to universe 6

Universe 2 buds off from a black hole in universe 1

Universe 7 is spawned by a Big Crunch in 5

A black hole in 2 creates universe 3

Our Universe may give rise to a whole series of universes

Universe 4 buds off when universe 2 collapses in a Big Crunch

Deliberately created

Black holes and Big Crunches can both provide "budding sites" where new universes can start. From one universe, they can spawn a network of independent universes. Although each baby universe is different, it will inherit some of its parent's "genes". This may be how our Universe came to be. American cosmologist Ed Harrison even suggests that our Universe is so ideally suited for the development of intelligent life that it may have been created by an advanced civilization in another universe. Perhaps the scientists in that universe reached the stage of making black holes in the lab, and one budded off to become our Universe. We may be just the result of someone's experiment!

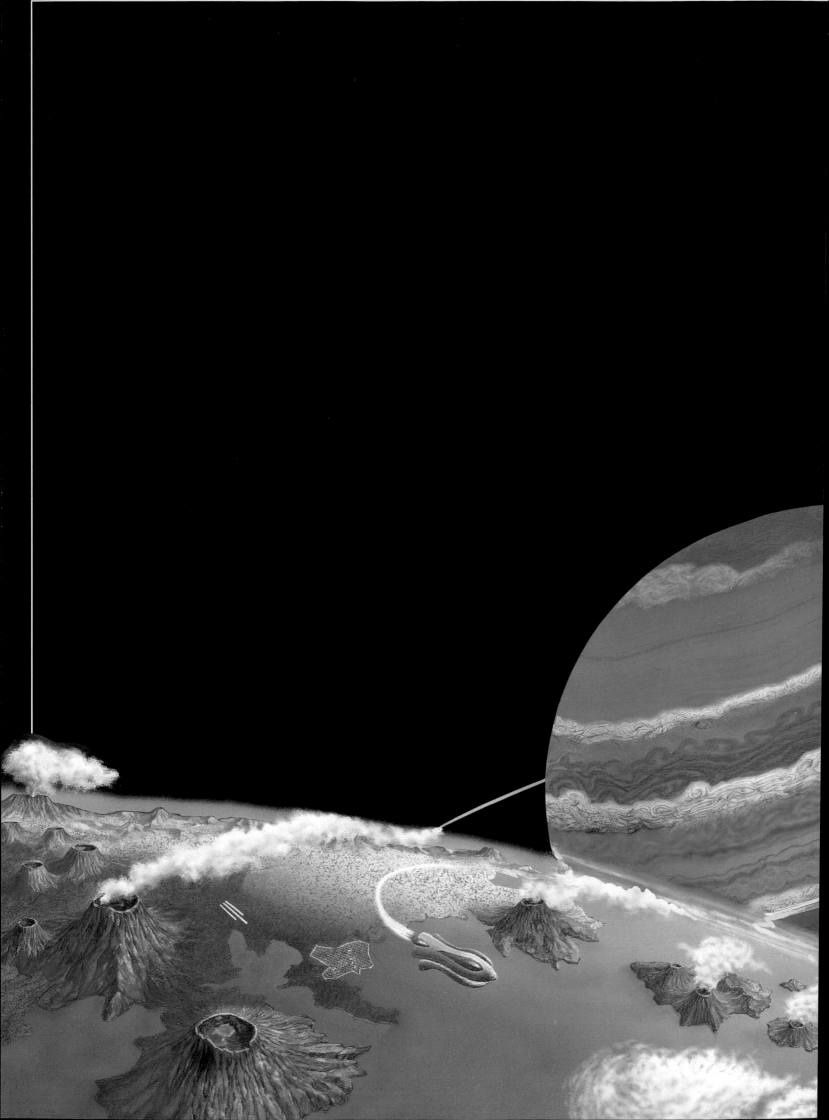

Is Anybody Out There?

Dᴏᴇs ɪɴᴛᴇʟʟɪɢᴇɴᴛ ʟɪғᴇ exist beyond our planet?

In the run-up to the Millennium this is the big question everyone wants answered.

Today life on Mars, UFOs, and extraterrestrials make headline news. But scientists have actually been searching for alien intelligence for nearly 40 years. Listening in with giant radio telescopes, they have been waiting – so far without success – for a message from another world. They have even beamed signals into space and placed messages on spacecraft in their quest for contact. The name of the game is SETI: the Search for Extraterrestrial Intelligence.

What is the likelihood of intelligent beings existing in other parts of the Universe? This section of the book investigates what the chances are. It examines the crucial question of how life on Earth came to exist; how many planets like ours there may be; whether there has ever been life on Mars; whether aliens have visited us; and even what they might look like.

Is Anybody Out There? charts our continuing quest to tune in to signals from intelligent lifeforms out there – from the early days of the enigmatic "Wow!" signal to today's plans to build a dedicated SETI facility on the far side of the Moon. And it raises the ultimate question: What should we do when we finally get the message? Should we reply – or would the dangers of contact with alien intelligence be too much for the human race?

Is this what they look like?

ALIENS. THEY LEAP OUT FROM THE PAGES of science fiction magazines, invade our homes through the TV set, and become stars on the big screen. But do they really exist? Until recently, most scientists would not even consider the possibility of alien life. Now we know so much about our place in the Universe that the alien question won't go away. Earth is an ordinary planet, circling an average star: if life happened here, then why not elsewhere? But one thing's for sure. It won't look anything like the crowd of movie aliens here: in many cases their humanoid appearance owes more to limited film and TV budgets than it does to the way biology would evolve on a truly alien world.

As well as imagining aliens, writers and artists earlier this century dreamed of the future of planet Earth. In the magazine story "Cities in the Air" (1929), New York rises above pollution on an anti-gravity cushion.

Flash Gordon (1936)
Faced with an enemy like this, the fearless Flash Gordon could hardly know if he was battling aliens or a troop of Teutonic soldiers.

Man From Planet X (1951)
A twist to the usual idea of alien visitation, this film featured an extraterrestrial visitor whose intentions were genuinely friendly. However, the humans were anything but.

Flash Gordon (1940)
This later alien, capturing Dale Arden, may have a suitably extraterrestrial head, but still a remarkably humanoid body.

The Day the Earth Stood Still (1951)
An alien and his robot land on Earth to protest against nuclear testing. He is similar enough to us to disguise himself as a human.

Zombies of the Stratosphere (1952)
Aliens again visit Earth in vaguely humanoid shapes, including a Martian who saves the Earth from devastation.

Invaders from Mars (1953)
Apart from its hands and eyes, this alien – here capturing and brainwashing the inhabitants of a small town – could pass for human.

Them (1954)
It looks the most alien creature on this page, but ironically this monster is merely a terrestrial ant mutated by leakages of radiation from nuclear tests.

One of a series of cartoons published in the *New York Times* in 1835 depicting views of aliens on the Moon, allegedly obtained through a telescope in South Africa.

Aliens in history

Many astronomers in the 17th and 18th centuries imagined that all the planets were inhabited by beings who, like us, took pleasure in food, music, and art. The 17th-century Dutch scientist Christiaan Huygens, who discovered Saturn's rings, suggested that Jupiter and Saturn were ideal worlds for sailors because they have so many moons to assist navigation. Other astronomers even believed that life could exist on the Sun! With increasing knowledge, those beliefs waned, only to return with a vengeance in the late 19th century, when the Martian "canals" were discovered. Surely these were built by intelligent Martians to irrigate a planet that was drying out? For the first time, the notion of alien life gripped the imagination of the public, and the fascination has never really gone away.

Close Encounters of the Third Kind (1977)
One of Steven Spielberg's early successes, this film turned fear of an alien invasion into religious joy at their coming. The shots of the pedestal-shaped Devil's Tower in Wyoming – the focus for the UFO activity – haunt viewers of the film forever.

Superman (1978)
Superman, the most popular superhero, was an alien baby sent to Earth for safety before his own planet, Krypton, exploded.

Star Trek (1979)
The film and TV series were more concerned with social and environmental messages than with the science of alien life – hence the humanoid aliens who often speak perfect English!

This Island Earth (1954)
These aliens, who abduct Earth scientists to save their own planet, may have strange hands and feet – but the size and shape of their bodies is rather familiar.

Invasion of the Star Creatures (1962)
They may have come from the stars, but the marauders have evolved in a manner remarkably similar to us, right down to their kneecaps!

Invaders from Mars (1986)
When the film was remade 30 years later, audiences expected invading Martians to look less human.

Spaced Invaders (1990)
A gang of Martians invades the Earth at Halloween: with figures and costumes like this, they didn't look much out of place!

91

The birth of life

OUR SEARCH FOR INTELLIGENT LIFE in the Universe must begin at home. Planet Earth is the only place where we know life exists. From its volcanic beginnings, the young Earth spawned the first microscopic living cells which evolved, over billions of years, into a wonderful richness of plants and animals. If we can understand how life on Earth was created from rocks, gas, and water, then we can start to surmise whether alien life may have arisen on other planets.

Violent beginnings

Some scientists believe the raw material for life was the gas spewing from volcanoes: simple molecules in the gas were welded into larger, more complex molecules by energy from lightning and, possibly, sunlight.

LIFE, CARBON, AND ORGANIC MOLECULES

Carbon atoms are the basis of all life, as they combine with each other and other atoms to make complex and versatile compounds. Such carbon compounds were first found in living cells, so chemists call them "organic". Astronomers have now found carbon-rich "organic molecules" in the Universe that have *not* been produced by life. They are often black, and are like coal or tar.

1 CHOKING "AIR"
Volcanic gases cloaked early Earth in a dense, choking atmosphere of water vapour, carbon dioxide, and nitrogen, with some methane, hydrogen, and ammonia. Split by lightning, these molecules regrouped as complex organic compounds, such as amino acids.

Atmosphere's ingredients

2 ATMOSPHERIC CHANGES
Water vapour condensed into a planet-wide rainstorm lasting millions of years. Most of the organic molecules created by lightning were washed into the oceans, leaving an "air" of carbon dioxide and nitrogen — similar to that of present-day Venus and Mars.

| 4,600 mya | 4,000 mya | 3,000 mya | 2,000 mya |

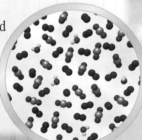

Over three billion years ago, organic molecules joined together to create the first forms of life. They were very simple creatures consisting of a single cell, rather like algae, bacteria, or amoebae.

THE ORIGINS OF LIFE

In 1953, American chemist Stanley Miller (b. 1930) put a mixture of gases — simulating Earth's early atmosphere — in a flask, and passed electric sparks through it overnight to mimic lightning. Water in the flask represented the early ocean. In the morning, Miller found the transparent gases had turned to an orange-brown "gunge" dissolved in the water. The experiment had created several new and complex compounds, including amino acids

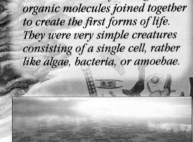

Stanley Miller — the first scientist to experiment with the origin of life.

PRIMEVAL SOUP

The organic molecules made in the atmosphere were washed into the oceans, forming a thin "primeval soup". In rockpools, the soup became concentrated and the amino acids joined to make proteins. Other molecules reacted to build deoxyribonucleic acid (DNA) while fatty molecules formed a protective membrane that surrounded everything. The first living cells were born.

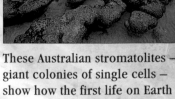

These Australian stromatolites — giant colonies of single cells — show how the first life on Earth may have looked.

Inside the cell

All life on Earth – animal, plant, or microbe – is made from the same types of organic molecules, containing some of the most common elements in the Universe: carbon, hydrogen, oxygen, and nitrogen. They are packaged into microscopic cells that all work in a surprisingly similar way. The different parts of the cell probably started as "mini cells" which teamed up to work more effectively.

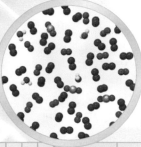

The human body is made of 50 billion cells. Skin cells, nerve cells, and muscle cells are all similar inside.

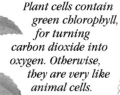

Plant cells contain green chlorophyll, for turning carbon dioxide into oxygen. Otherwise, they are very like animal cells.

Mitochondrion

MITOCHONDRION
The mitochondrion is the cell's powerhouse – it creates energy by "burning" sugar in oxygen. Instead of producing a flame, a slow-motion reaction releases a continual stream of energy-packed molecules that deliver power where it's needed.

RIBOSOME
The ribosome is the factory – it assembles the small "building-block" molecules, amino acids, into proteins. Some proteins form the cell's structures; others, called enzymes, control the reactions that keep the cell functioning.

Ribosome

NUCLEUS
The nucleus contains the long double helix of DNA, which holds all the chemical information for everything the cell does.

DNA

REPRODUCTION
When a cell divides, the inherited DNA ensures that the "daughter cells" are identical to the parent.

3 TURNING THE TABLES
Over the next 2 billion years, evolving plants turned most of the carbon dioxide into oxygen. Having been created from atmospheric gases, life changed the atmosphere to suit its own requirements!

4 UNIQUE ATMOSPHERE
Life created an atmosphere, unique in the Solar System, of mainly nitrogen and oxygen. In the upper atmosphere, oxygen atoms formed the ozone layer, protecting the surface from the Sun's lethal rays.

Time in millions of years ago (mya)

1,000 mya

500 mya

Ancestor of fish

Ozone layer allowed life to flourish on land.

EARLY TRIALS
The early cells eventually learnt to work together to build up complex plants and animals. Earth's oceans were alive with a weird collection of biological experiments 570 million years ago. Most did not survive; but one or two became the ancestors of the fish.

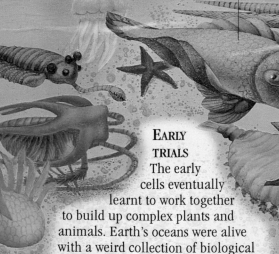

ON TO LAND
Some fish evolved into amphibians, moving from the protective ocean to land, now screened by the ozone layer. With them went some seaweeds, which eventually became grass, trees, and flowers. A number of amphibians evolved into reptiles, dinosaurs, birds, mammals, and eventually humans.

Impact!

L IFE IN THE UNIVERSE is constantly under threat from bombardment. In its early days, Earth was pounded by rocky or metallic asteroids and frozen comets – debris left over from the building of the Sun and planets. But this apparent threat to emerging life was a blessing in disguise. By wiping out weak forms of life, bombardment encouraged stronger, more versatile strains to evolve. Some scientists now believe that most of the Earth's water and the other raw materials of life did not come from volcanoes, but were dumped on our planet from space.

Comets: bringers of life?

Comets have long been associated with doom and destruction. In the past, when no one knew what comets were, the appearance of a comet in the sky – a ghostly dagger poised to strike – must have been terrifying. But spaceprobes, such as *Giotto*, have revealed that comets could be bringers of life, because they contain vast quantities of organic molecules and water. In its distant home, far from the Sun, a comet is a frozen lump of ice and rock a few tens of kilometres across. But as it plummets towards the heat of the Sun, its evaporating gases expand into a huge head of steam, swept away by the solar wind into a glowing tail millions of kilometres long.

Comets striking Earth were more common in the distant past when "construction site" debris was more plentiful. Today, major impacts occur at roughly 100 million year intervals.

Comets in their natural state mostly reside in the Oort Cloud – a huge, spherical reservoir of millions of frozen bodies stretching perhaps halfway to the nearest stars.

Europe's Giotto *probe skimmed past Halley's Comet in 1986. It revealed jets of gas spewing out of an icy lump 10 km (6 miles) across and coated, to astronomers' surprise, in dark organic "tar".*

FRED — THE MAVERICK

Sir Fred Hoyle, although a brilliant scientist, can hardly be described as conventional. One of his ideas is that life arrived fully formed – possibly even hatched – in "eggs" that were brought to Earth in comets. Another is that the dark, sooty "dust" that collects together into huge clouds in space is in fact freeze-dried bacteria; these cause mass epidemics, such as AIDS and flu, on Earth.

British astronomer Fred Hoyle (b. 1915) is chiefly famous for his "Steady State" theory, which holds that the Universe has no beginning and no end.

Frozen into an icy comet is a cornucopia of organic molecules. Comets may have "seeded" the Earth with these raw materials for life.

Once a comet becomes trapped in a close orbit around the Sun, it steadily boils away. After about 250,000 years, it is reduced to tiny grains of dust.

The young Earth – and presumably other planets – were blitzed by cosmic impact. But these also delivered water and dark patches of organic molecules.

COSMIC RUBBLE

The gap between the orbits of Mars and Jupiter is littered with thousands of lumps of rock and metal, called asteroids. The strong gravity of Jupiter stops the asteroids from assembling into a planet.

What wiped out the dinosaurs?

The dinosaurs – which had ruled Earth for over 100 million years – became extinct 65 million years ago, along with many other species. At the same time, rocks worldwide were enriched with vast quantities of the element iridium, which is rare on our planet but common in comets and asteroids. It is thought that an object 10 km (6 miles) across smashed into Yucatan in Mexico, where there is now a large crater. The huge explosion sent up a pall of iridium-rich dust, blotting out the Sun for months. Plant life was devastated, and few animals survived.

Dinosaurs were probably wiped out by a cosmic impact – one of several that are thought to have caused mass extinctions.

One in the eye for Jupiter

In March 1993, the veteran American comet-hunting team of Carolyn and Gene Shoemaker and David Levy discovered a comet near Jupiter. It looked totally strange – like a string of pearls. Astronomers were astonished to discover that it had been pulled apart into more than 20 pieces by Jupiter's enormous gravity. They were even more amazed to find that Comet Shoemaker-Levy 9 was on a collision course with the planet. In July 1994, the fragments rammed into Jupiter at 216,000 km/h (135,000 mph), producing colossal explosions.

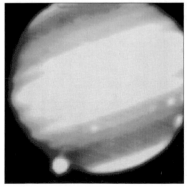

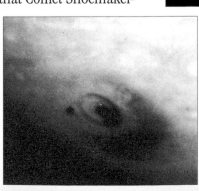

Infrared (heat) image of one of the 1994 impacts: some of the comet's fragments were 4 km (2.5 miles) across.

The aftermath, imaged by the *Hubble Space Telescope*: the impact left "black eyes" of organic molecules.

SPACEGUARD!

Although most asteroids live beyond Mars, some – maybe as many as 2,000 – have orbits that bring them close to Earth. One day, an asteroid like this could hit us, and astronomers are busy tracking them down. The international "Project Spaceguard" would be activated if an asteroid was bent on collision – by exploding a nuclear warhead nearby, the asteroid would be pushed off course.

Nuclear warheads

Exploding warhead alters course of approaching asteroid.

On the trail of Martians

Planet Mars is the nearest plausible home for alien life. Rumours of intelligent Martians began in the 19th century with sightings of "canals" on Mars and have been stoked by incidents such as a terrifyingly real Orson Welles radio play in 1939 "reporting" a Martian invasion of Earth! The latest surge of optimism came with the possible discovery of fossils from Mars (pages 98–99). But the "ups" have been balanced by deep "downs". The first spaceprobe images of the planet showed a barren and lifeless world, and astronomers' hopes were dashed.

Bombarded planet

As late as the 1950s, astronomers were hopeful that some primitive plant life, such as mosses or lichens, might live on Mars. But the first spaceprobe pictures were bitterly disappointing. They revealed an almost airless world – heavily pockmarked with impact craters – that looked more like the Moon than the Earth. But the probes had been surveying just one hemisphere of the planet – it later emerged that Mars has a far more interesting side.

Mars' barren, cratered surface was first revealed by NASA's Mariner 4 spaceprobe in 1965.

Panorama of present-day Martian landscape.

HUNTING DOWN THE MARTIANS

In 1877, Italian astronomer Giovanni Schiaparelli reported seeing long, straight lines on Mars. He called them "canali" (Italian for channels). But American amateur astronomer Percival Lowell – a rich Boston businessman – mistranslated this as "canals" (deliberately constructed watercourses). Mars was drying out, he maintained, and intelligent Martians living on the equator had built the canals to bring water from the polar caps in an attempt to save their world.

Mars-obsessed Lowell built a large observatory in Arizona dedicated to observing the planet.

The canals turned out to be optical illusions, caused by the eye's tendency to "see" geometrical shapes in faint detail. Spaceprobe images show no trace of them.

VIKING: IN SEARCH OF LIFE

In 1971, *Mariner 9* saw Mars' other side. The first probe to orbit the Red Planet, it revealed a hemisphere in which giant volcanoes and colossal chasms combined to produce one of the most dramatic – and Earth-like – landscapes in the Solar System. But most important of all, *Mariner 9* discovered traces of dried-up river beds. If there had ever been water on Mars, then life might have started. These discoveries spurred NASA to build two *Viking* craft – the first spaceprobes to be sent to another planet in search of life. Each craft consisted of an *Orbiter* and a *Lander*.

Both Landers touched down safely in Mars' northern hemisphere in mid-1976. Some 6,460 km (4,010 miles) apart, they were almost on opposite sides of the planet.

The long arm scooped up soil to be analysed within the Lander.

Mars' soil is red because it's rusty – a result of the water that flowed in the past.

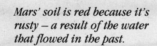

Robot laboratory

The *Viking* scientists thought the Martian soil might contain microscopic cells, resembling bacteria or yeast. To check for life, each *Lander* carried out four experiments in a laboratory the size of a large wastepaper basket. The results show reactive chemicals in the soil – but no life.

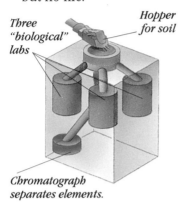

Three "biological" labs

Hopper for soil

Chromatograph separates elements.

FORENSIC SCIENCE

Like a police lab analysing traces from a crime, the gas chromatograph broke down the soil into its basic atoms. It detected many chemical elements, including iron, silicon, and oxygen. But there was no sign of carbon – the basic building block of life.

Nutrient supply

Gas detector

Helium

Soil wetted with sugar produces gas.

FERMENTATION

In the labelled release experiment, any yeasts present would generate gases as they do in fermenting wine. Gas did pour off, but production soon stopped, indicating a chemical reaction.

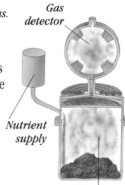

Gas detector

Nutrient supply

Gas produced for a short time only

COOKING

A bright lamp in the pyrolytic release experiment encouraged any plant-like cells to grow and multiply. After five days, the soil was heated, and a detector "sniffed out" any aromas from freshly cooked cells. The results were inconclusive.

Artificial sun

"Cooking aromas" broken down to simple gases

Gas detector

Heat breaks down the chemicals in the soil.

BREAKING WIND

All cells produce gases as they feed on nutrients. In the gas exchange experiment, the Martian soil produced gas when it was wetted with sugar solution. But the gas died away rapidly: a sure sign of merely a chemical reaction.

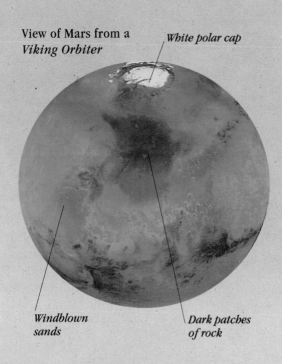

View of Mars from a Viking Orbiter

White polar cap

Windblown sands

Dark patches of rock

Mars: the sterile world

Mars today appears to be a lifeless world. The shifting dark markings, once thought to be growing vegetation, are now known to be areas of rocks periodically covered and uncovered by windblown sands. The water that was once plentiful on the planet is now frozen into the soil as permafrost; and the white polar caps are made largely of frozen carbon dioxide. Most telling of all, Mars now has a planet-wide ozone hole. It allows ultraviolet radiation from the Sun to penetrate all the way to the surface – sterilizing the soil and leaving any emergent life without a chance of survival.

Two cameras provided stereoscopic views.

The antenna sent signals to the Viking Orbiter, *busy mapping the planet from high above, which relayed them to Earth.*

A meteorology boom checked out wind speed and air temperature.

Particles of red soil, suspended in the thin air, tinge Mars' sky salmon-pink.

ROBOT ON THE RED PLANET

The two *Viking Landers* were the most sophisticated spaceprobes ever built. Each was a truly intelligent robot, with stereoscopic colour vision, chemistry and biology laboratories, a weather station, and a communications dish.

Mars: abode of life?

ALTHOUGH BARREN NOW, Mars was a very different world in the past. Close-up scrutiny by spaceprobes has revealed evidence that Mars once had tumbling streams and a substantial atmosphere. Billions of years ago, the planet itself was far more active, with volcanoes and Mars-quakes, and it was a lot warmer. Scientists have even proposed that there may have been shallow oceans. In these conditions – similar to those prevailing on the young Earth – life may well have got under way.

Mars attacks!

Young Mars was a violent place. Volcanoes belched, while Mars-quakes shook the ground. Together with the abundant water and thick atmosphere, all the ingredients were present for the creation of life. Even frequent comet and meteorite impacts supplied fresh materials. But in the end, this rain of bombardment may have put paid to life's chances – by blasting away most of the atmosphere of this small, low-gravity planet.

HERE'S LOOKIN' AT YOU
The "Face on Mars" has been described as a huge artefact from a lost Martian civilization, like a vast Egyptian pyramid. However, seen from a different perspective, as in this computer-generated image (below left), the 1.5 km (1 mile)-long "face" shows itself for what it is: a naturally wind-eroded hill, one of several in the vicinity.

The wind-eroded hill shows up on this computer-generated image.

Bombardments may have helped to create life, but on Mars they may have also destroyed it.

The same panorama as seen on pages 96–97, but 3 billion years earlier. Young Mars resembled early Earth, with active volcanoes and fast-flowing rivers.

Volcanic eruptions and impacts of icy comets provided water for the rivers that once flowed across Mars' surface.

The Martians have landed!

In August 1996, NASA scientists caused a worldwide sensation when they announced that tiny structures found in a meteorite blasted out of Mars might be fossils of primitive life. The fossils were estimated to be 3.6 billion years old. But when the excitement died down, other scientists examined the evidence – and concluded that the "fossils" were more likely to be of mineral, rather than animal, origin.

MESSENGER FROM MARS

ALH84001 – the rock from Mars – landed in Antarctica 13,000 years ago and was preserved in the ice sheet. It is one of 12 Martian meteorites currently under investigation.

MARTIAN CREEPY-CRAWLY?

Magnified 100,000 times, these bacterium-shaped "fossils" discovered in ALH84001 are one-hundredth the diameter of a human hair – on the small side for a living being.

Mars Pathfinder braked its entry into the Martian atmosphere with a heat-resistant aeroshell.

On reaching the lower layers of the atmosphere, it deployed a huge parachute.

NASA's Global Surveyor kept a watch on Mars from orbit.

Japan's Planet-B will study Mars' upper atmosphere.

Mars – the search continues

After a lull of more than 20 years – when there were no successful missions to Mars – a veritable flotilla of spaceprobes was targeted towards the Red Planet in the late 1990s. First in the race were NASA's *Mars Pathfinder* and *Global Surveyor*. They will be followed by a series of American, Russian-European, and Japanese spacecraft. These will drop penetrators to pierce deep into the soil and deploy balloons and rovers to comb the entire Martian surface for signs of life.

On landing, protective "petals" unfolded to reveal the scientific instruments.

Mars Pathfinder landed in an ancient flood-channel littered with huge boulders once carried by raging torrents of water.

Artist's impression of first Mars base

There's now little doubt that the next destination for the human race is Mars. Some experts believe that the first crewed mission will take place before 2020. Within 100 years of this landing, the first Martian bases will be built.

Mars Pathfinder carried the first robot rover to another planet – named "Sojourner" (traveller) after Sojourner Truth (1797–1883), a freed slave who spoke out for women's rights.

Mars' volcanoes may have been active until only a few million years ago.

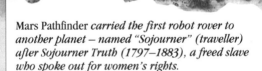

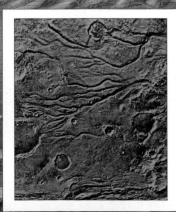

VANISHED RIVERS

Long, curved channels photographed by the *Viking Orbiters* look like dried-up river beds. These water courses must have been an impressive sight in the planet's youth. Some were over 100 km (75 miles) wide – a result of flash floods. But as the atmosphere ebbed away, the planet grew colder and the water froze into the soil as permafrost.

Fish on Jupiter

THE OBVIOUS PLACE TO SEARCH FOR LIFE in the Solar System may be Mars, but there are other possibilities. Some planets can be ruled out altogether: Mercury and Venus are too hot; Uranus, Neptune, and Pluto are too cold. But Jupiter and Saturn, along with their vast families of moons, may just be in with a chance – after all, life can exist in some pretty extreme environments on Earth. Attention currently focuses on Jupiter's moons, which are "pummelled" by Jupiter's gravity – making them warmer than they should be this far from the Sun.

Waterworld?

Dazzlingly white and smooth as a billiard ball, Europa is unlike any other moon in the Solar System. Close-up images from NASA's *Galileo* spaceprobe suggest it is covered in shifting ice floes, like arctic pack ice. Some scientists believe that an ocean lies below, warmed by eruptions from undersea volcanoes. Earth has similar thermal vents on the ocean floor, around which exotic creatures live. In his novel *2010*, British science fiction author Arthur C. Clarke imagined lifeforms on Europa. He may have been prophetically accurate.

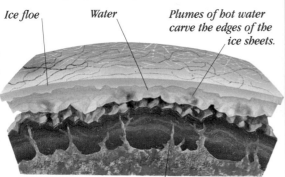

Ice floe   *Water*   *Plumes of hot water carve the edges of the ice sheets.*

Under Europa's icy surface, a huge ocean may be home to life that thrives on volcanic heat instead of sunlight.

Heat from the core rises through thermal vents ("undersea volcanoes") to heat the water.

By Jove!

Jupiter is by far the biggest planet in the Solar System – so large that all the other planets, or 1,300 Earths, could fit inside it. Unlike the inner planets, such as Earth or Mars, it is made almost completely of gases, including organic molecules such as methane and acetylene. In the centre is a small rocky core, heated by the weight of the overlying layers to 35,000°C (63,000°F), and so Jupiter is warmer than would be expected at 778 million km (483 million miles) from the Sun. The planet is surrounded by 16 moons, four of which – Io, Europa, Ganymede, and Callisto – are similar in size to the planets Mercury and Pluto.

CALLISTO   *Valhalla*

Callisto is the most heavily cratered of all Jupiter's moons, with one crater – Valhalla – measuring 300 km (185 miles) across. It looks like Earth's Moon but is made of ice.

DISTANT DRUMS

While spaceprobes hunt for life on, or in, our planetary neighbours, many scientists believe we will first be alerted to alien life by radio signals from much farther away. As the foldout pages underneath this page reveal, there's even a way of calculating how many advanced civilizations "out there" may be broadcasting to us.

Europa

The smooth, icy surface may conceal a huge, warm ocean.

Jupiter is stripy because of its rapid spin (it rotates in about 10 hours). The white "zones" are ice crystals high in its atmosphere; the coloured belts may be coloured by organic compounds.

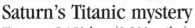

Saturn's Titanic mystery

Titan, at 5,150 km (3,200 miles) across, is Saturn's largest moon. It is the only moon in the Solar System with a thick atmosphere, composed mainly of nitrogen, like Earth's air. *Voyager 1*, specially targeted to fly close by in 1980, could see nothing through impenetrable cloud cover, but it did confirm the presence of methane. Scientists have speculated that Titan might be like "an early Earth in deep freeze", with organic molecules frozen on its surface. If warmed by a nearby volcano, perhaps they could combine to make life.

Titan's orange clouds, seen here from Voyager 1, *are probably made of oily, organic droplets.*

Ganymede's ancient gnarled surface reveals a history of impacts and geological activity.

GANYMEDE
Ganymede, 5,260 km (3,270 miles) across, is the biggest moon in the Solar System. Although probably too cold for life, the *Galileo* probe has detected organic molecules on its surface.

Io is the most active moon in the Solar System, with still-erupting volcanoes which create local hotspots of up to 1,500°C (2,725°F) on its surface.

Io
Wracked by volcanic eruptions, Io's surface is forever changing. It is heated internally by the pull of Jupiter's gravity, causing plumes of sulphur to shoot 300 km (185 miles) into space.

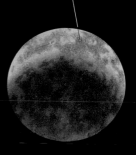

The Great Red Spot is a storm big enough to swallow three Earths. The red colour is due to phosphorus, an element essential to living organisms.

PIERCING THE VEIL
In 2004, the *Cassini* spaceprobe will arrive at Saturn. Its subprobe, *Huygens*, will plunge into Titan's clouds and image the surface. Scientists believe it will find a world with lakes of liquid methane and ethane – like natural gas on Earth – with rich accumulations of organic molecules, and mountains which may be active volcanoes. There's a faint chance that primitive bacteria might have evolved in the warmth of the volcanic vents.

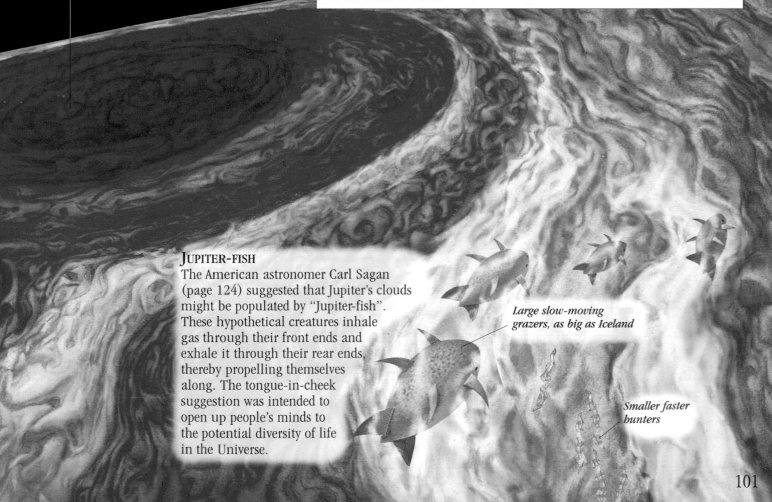

JUPITER-FISH
The American astronomer Carl Sagan (page 124) suggested that Jupiter's clouds might be populated by "Jupiter-fish". These hypothetical creatures inhale gas through their front ends and exhale it through their rear ends, thereby propelling themselves along. The tongue-in-cheek suggestion was intended to open up people's minds to the potential diversity of life in the Universe.

Large slow-moving grazers, as big as Iceland

Smaller faster hunters

Have they visited us?

L IFE ELSEWHERE IN OUR SOLAR SYSTEM — if it exists at all — would be merely "green slime": certainly nothing we would want to communicate with. But could there be life in solar systems beyond our own? Many people think so. Some even believe that there are civilizations so advanced that they can build starships to conquer the vast gulfs of space, and that these aliens have not only visited Earth, but left evidence behind to prove it. On this spread are some of the most persuasive examples of alien visitations, from ancient lines in the deserts of Peru to UFO sightings. But on investigation, the evidence for them being alien always breaks down.

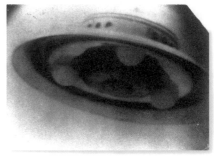

California-based mystic George Adamski caused a sensation in the 1950s when he claimed to have been abducted to Venus in a flying saucer. On close inspection, it turned out to be made of chicken feeders and bottle coolers.

Spacemen in history

Believers in alien visitations maintain that there is a great deal of archaeological and historical evidence to back their claim that Earth has been the focus of numerous extra-terrestrial landings. They point to the sophistication of the pyramids in Egypt and Mexico, the complexity of the Nazca Lines in Peru, and the sheer scale of the Easter Island statues — primitive people, they argue, could not have managed such gargantuan feats. And they comb the Bible for passages that could be interpreted as alien sightings, or even the aftermath of a nuclear explosion. But there are equally valid down-to-Earth explanations for all these strange phenomena.

Old rock paintings from the Nazca Plains in Peru contain figures that are claimed to represent aliens — there is also a close resemblance to the traditional costume in that area.

An ancient cave painting in Italy of a figure with domed headgear. However, it is more likely to be an ancient headdress rather than, as some claim, a space helmet.

STATUES FROM OUTER SPACE

Some people maintain that the statues on Easter Island are so massive that they could only have been carved, and then raised, by aliens using advanced technology. But Thor Heyerdahl, a Norwegian anthropologist, restaged their construction using local people and old stone tools. He concluded that each statue would take a year to build — well within the power of human beings.

The Pyramids of Giza are aligned precisely north-south, with interior passages pointing towards the stars of Orion. But this is an indication of long-established human intelligence, rather than alien visitors.

Flying saucers

In the summer of 1947, US pilot Kenneth Arnold was amazed to see nine silvery discs skimming at nearly 2,000 km/h (1,250 mph) over the Cascade Mountains in Washington State. A reporter nicknamed them "flying saucers". Since then, there have been thousands of sightings of "unidentified flying objects" (UFOs). But despite considerable investigation, there is still no explanation of what they might be.

Almost certainly, the vast majority of UFOs are natural phenomena – meteors or even ball lightning – that are misinterpreted. This metallic-looking object photographed by Paul Trent in 1950 over his farm in Oregon remains inexplicable, but there is no evidence that it came from another planet.

CROP CIRCLES

Every summer since the late 1980s, flattened circles and other geometrical shapes have suddenly appeared in cornfields all over Britain. Some people believe they are the landing sites of flying saucers. But they could equally well be the result of summer-time revels by students or young farmers.

Over the years, crop circles have been growing more complex – a testimony to the skill of their human creators!

NAZCA LINES

The Nazca Desert in southern Peru is criss-crossed with a bewildering pattern of lines and geometrical shapes so enormous that they only make sense when seen from the air. Were they, as some claim, runways for UFOs? Probably not: UFOs would have got stuck in the soft sand. The lines are probably of religious origin, designed so that the gods of the sky would notice the people below. The Nazca Lines were made by removing stones from the desert to reveal the lighter subsoil.

EGYPTIAN PYRAMIDS

The Great Pyramids at Giza are built on such a majestic scale that some believe their construction was the work of visiting aliens. But the Egyptian civilization dates back to 5,000 BC. Archaeologists have now established that pyramid construction techniques evolved over the millennia, leading to the magnificent examples that have survived to this day.

In the Bible, Ezekiel describes the appearance in the sky of a fiery object with whirling wheels which spoke to him.

ALIENS IN THE BIBLE

The many accounts of visitations by angels in the Bible are sometimes interpreted as alien sightings. Even the destruction of Sodom and Gomorrah is said to have been caused by a nuclear explosion, which turned Lot's wife into a pillar of salt! But the best-attested case of a UFO sighting in the Bible is in Ezekiel. His UFO was probably a series of parhelia, or "sundogs" – bright images of the Sun refracted by high-level clouds.

NEW WORLD PYRAMIDS

The pyramids of Mexico and the carvings within them are sometimes interpreted as the work of an alien civilization. The carvings are compared to images of astronauts driving spacecraft, and the pyramids lauded as engineering miracles way ahead of their time. But the carvings are simply intricate religious imagery, and the pyramids are elaborate stone cairns used to bury the dead.

Worlds beyond

To track down intelligent life means reaching out beyond our Solar System. In particular, it involves finding planets around other stars: sites where life could develop. But even the nearest stars are a million times farther away than our Sun – and while planets are small and dark, stars are big and bright. So the task is like looking for moths circling streetlights in New York from the distance of London. But in the past few years, astronomers have developed more sensitive equipment, and are confident that they have located at least a dozen "extrasolar" planets. So far only massive planets – as heavy as Jupiter – have been found; planets like the Earth may also be there, but are too lightweight to be detected with current techniques.

It takes all types
Planetary systems are thought to be born in a swirling disc of gas and dust, and astronomers once assumed that they would all look like our Solar System – with small planets close in and larger ones farther out. The newly discovered systems look anything but.

Beta Pictoris, with its disc of debris, may be too young to have formed planets yet.

Didier Queloz and Michel Mayor: first to discover an extrasolar planet.

Pulling power
The number of extrasolar planets now known exceeds the number of planets in the Solar System, but no one has actually seen them. These worlds have been pinpointed because of their gravitational pull on their parent stars – and to detect this, the planets must be massive.

New worlds
On October 6, 1995, Michel Mayor and Didier Queloz of the Geneva Observatory in Switzerland, announced that they had discovered a planet orbiting the sun-like star 51 Pegasi. Three months later, Geoff Marcy and Paul Butler found planets circling two more stars, 47 Ursae Majoris and 70 Virginis.

Paul Butler and Geoff Marcy have evidence for the existence of at least eight extrasolar planets.

The right stuff
The sun-like star, 47 Ursae Majoris – 35 light years away, in the constellation of the Great Bear – was found by American astronomers Geoff Marcy and Paul Butler to have a planet weighing in at 2.3 times the mass of Jupiter. It lies at twice the distance from its star as the Earth does from the Sun – where it may still be warm enough for liquid water to exist and for life to develop. If, as in our Solar System, giant planets are surrounded by extensive retinues of moons, life might have started on one of these as well.

Planet of 47 Ursae Majoris

A moon circling the planet belonging to 47 Ursae Majoris could have volcanoes, water, plants, and intelligent life.

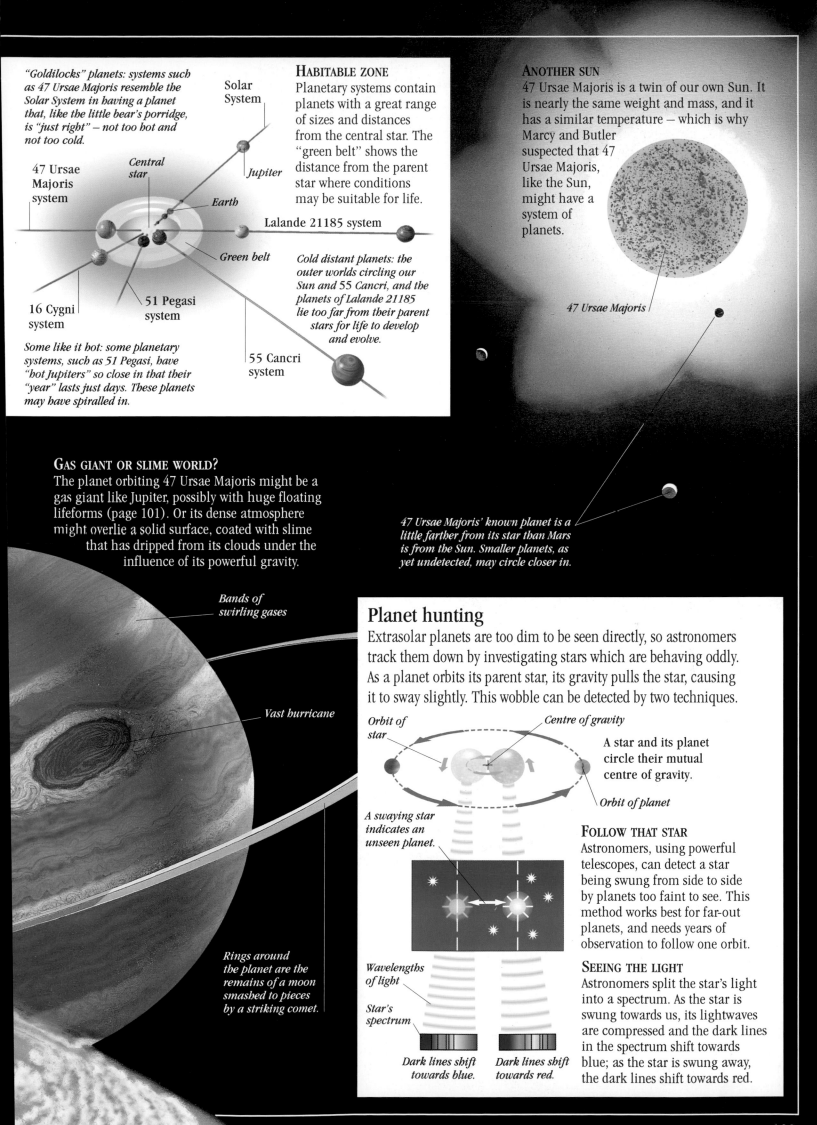

"Goldilocks" planets: systems such as 47 Ursae Majoris resemble the Solar System in having a planet that, like the little bear's porridge, is "just right" – not too hot and not too cold.

Solar System

47 Ursae Majoris system

Central star

Jupiter

Earth

16 Cygni system

51 Pegasi system

Green belt

Some like it hot: some planetary systems, such as 51 Pegasi, have "hot Jupiters" so close in that their "year" lasts just days. These planets may have spiralled in.

HABITABLE ZONE

Planetary systems contain planets with a great range of sizes and distances from the central star. The "green belt" shows the distance from the parent star where conditions may be suitable for life.

Lalande 21185 system

Cold distant planets: the outer worlds circling our Sun and 55 Cancri, and the planets of Lalande 21185 lie too far from their parent stars for life to develop and evolve.

55 Cancri system

ANOTHER SUN

47 Ursae Majoris is a twin of our own Sun. It is nearly the same weight and mass, and it has a similar temperature – which is why Marcy and Butler suspected that 47 Ursae Majoris, like the Sun, might have a system of planets.

47 Ursae Majoris

GAS GIANT OR SLIME WORLD?

The planet orbiting 47 Ursae Majoris might be a gas giant like Jupiter, possibly with huge floating lifeforms (page 101). Or its dense atmosphere might overlie a solid surface, coated with slime that has dripped from its clouds under the influence of its powerful gravity.

47 Ursae Majoris' known planet is a little farther from its star than Mars is from the Sun. Smaller planets, as yet undetected, may circle closer in.

Bands of swirling gases

Vast hurricane

Rings around the planet are the remains of a moon smashed to pieces by a striking comet.

Planet hunting

Extrasolar planets are too dim to be seen directly, so astronomers track them down by investigating stars which are behaving oddly. As a planet orbits its parent star, its gravity pulls the star, causing it to sway slightly. This wobble can be detected by two techniques.

Orbit of star

Centre of gravity

A star and its planet circle their mutual centre of gravity.

Orbit of planet

A swaying star indicates an unseen planet.

FOLLOW THAT STAR

Astronomers, using powerful telescopes, can detect a star being swung from side to side by planets too faint to see. This method works best for far-out planets, and needs years of observation to follow one orbit.

SEEING THE LIGHT

Astronomers split the star's light into a spectrum. As the star is swung towards us, its lightwaves are compressed and the dark lines in the spectrum shift towards blue; as the star is swung away, the dark lines shift towards red.

Wavelengths of light

Star's spectrum

Dark lines shift towards blue.

Dark lines shift towards red.

What a difference 10g makes

IF LIFE HAS EVOLVED on any of the newly discovered planets in our Galaxy, what would it look like? All lifeforms, no matter how alien, would share some characteristics: eyes, ears, mouth, and reproductive organs, for instance. But the position of these organs would not necessarily bear any resemblance to the human layout. Environment, too, has a part to play. Creatures would evolve differently on the small world "Moo", where the pull of gravity (0.1g) is only one-tenth of Earth's, and on the giant planet "Peg", where the gravity is 10g.

THE ALTERNATIVE HUMAN

You might have looked like this! "Arnold" was designed by a biologist to show how life might have evolved on Earth if different creatures had gained the upper hand 570 million years ago (page 93). The environment that led to Arnold was identical to the conditions that gave rise to humans.

Arnold has three eyes on stalks, three arms (one a thick but sensitive feeler), and three legs.

The world Moo

Moo is a moon circling the giant planet Peg (the worlds seen on the previous spread). Because it is small, it has low gravity. Except at star-rise and star-set, it is also cold, because its star spends a good deal of time eclipsed behind giant Peg. But lifeforms on Moo have adapted to these conditions. They grow high, curl up when cold, have big eyes to see in the dark, and have developed efficient ways of breathing in the thin air.

Moo-man stands with his gills stretched, enjoying the warmth of star-rise.

Moo-creatures breathe through huge branching gills – the air is so thin, that breathing passages and lungs are useless.

A set of large eyes opens in dim light, while a circlet of compound eyes gives all-round vision in bright light.

They "speak" by rubbing their tentacles together. Their mouths are just above the ground, close to the plants they feed on.

Moo-woman curls protectively around her new offspring, budded from the end of a tentacle. When it matures, the offspring will separate to lead an independent existence.

Moo-creatures reproduce sexually, by interlocking specialized tentacles.

Star-rise in the 47 Ursae Majoris system. The star is about to pass behind the planet Peg, leaving Moo dark and cold.

DAILY ECLIPSE

With its thin air, the sky above Moo always looks dark: you can easily see the faint glowing atmosphere of its parent star 47 Ursae Majoris. Soon after star-rise, the star will disappear behind the giant planet Peg, and Moo will be enveloped in a long eclipse until the star emerges shortly before star-set.

Moo's plant life is purple, because it photosynthesizes a different form of chlorophyll.

Water is essential to life on Moo. Strange as they look, the creatures on Moo are made of water – the universal solvent – and organic compounds that are rather similar to the ingredients of life on Earth.

The watery oceans on Moo would be familiar to us.

The planet Peg

Peg is a giant world with high gravity and a dense, choking atmosphere. But underneath, it has a sludgy surface populated by millions of Peg-creatures. They are very different from the inhabitants of Moo. The 10g gravity and intense pressure makes them very flat, and they are sightless – the thick atmosphere is so foggy that eyes are useless. Instead, Peg-creatures establish their whereabouts by using sonar, like bats on Earth.

To withstand the pressure, the Peg-creatures are massively fortified, like submersibles that descend to the bottom of Earth's deepest oceans.

Horn-like apertures on the back emit sonar pulses for location.

A slit-like mouth scoops up the sludgy soil and sifts it for microorganisms to eat.

Massive paddle-like legs propel the creatures across the slimy surface.

The body features protrude very little. The creatures are also very sluggish, so that they don't overheat.

The fish on Moo are a familiar shape, because the form of their bodies is dictated by the buoyancy of the water rather than gravity.

Talking alien

Aliens will certainly look very different from us, and think differently, too. And, unlike movie aliens, they won't speak fluent American — so how are we ever going to communicate with them? Phil Morrison, an American physicist and expert on extra-terrestrial life, believes that aliens would communicate in codes designed to be broken as easily as possible. Here are some of our own attempts to send easily decipherable messages from Earth to the stars.

If, in 25,000 years, someone in M13 receives the Arecibo message, we'll have to wait 25,000 years for the reply.

Message to M13

In 1974, astronomers at Arecibo in Puerto Rico sent a message from humankind to the stars. Lasting just three minutes, it was a signal consisting of 1,679 on-off pulses beamed towards M13, a dense ball of a million stars lying 25,000 light years away. An intelligent alien living there would realize that 1,679 is the product of two prime numbers, 23 and 73. Arranging the pulses into a rectangle 23 columns wide and 73 rows deep creates a pictogram explaining the basis of life on Earth.

PIONEERING MESSAGE

The first spaceprobes to leave the Solar System, *Pioneer 10* and *11*, both carried engraved plaques explaining who had sent them — the cosmic equivalent of the "message in a bottle". The plaques revealed the whereabouts of the Earth, the position of the Solar System, and the outlines of a man and a woman.

Arecibo's message with the 1,679 pulses rearranged in 73 rows of 23 columns to form a pictogram.

The wavy lines represent the radio waves beaming the signal from Arecibo into space. The peaks and troughs are separated by a wavelength of 12.6 cm.

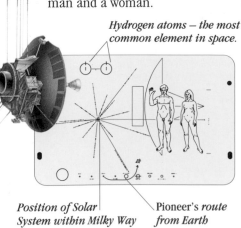

Hydrogen atoms — the most common element in space.

Position of Solar System within Milky Way

Pioneer's route from Earth

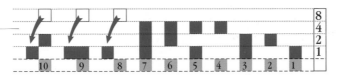

THINK OF A NUMBER
The first block shows, from right to left, the numbers 1 to 10 in binary code – the form computers use.

ELEMENTS OF LIFE
This block picks out five numbers: they are the atomic numbers (number of protons) of the most important elements of life.

15-Phosphorus

1-Hydrogen

8-Oxygen

6-Carbon

7-Nitrogen

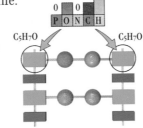

MAGIC MOLECULES
These blocks reveal the proportions of the five key elements in certain molecules – sugar (C_5H_7O coded green), phosphate (purple), and the nucleotides (orange) – making up the structure of DNA.

C_5H_7O C_5H_7O

THE DOUBLE HELIX
The two twisted strands show the "double helix" structure of DNA, the huge molecule that divides and replicates to pass on the "blueprint" of life.

IN A HUMAN IMAGE
The outline of a human – probably the most baffling image to an alien – is flanked by the world's population (left) and the human's height (right).

Height of a human: 14 wavelengths of the signal

Earth   *Sun*

Solar System with Earth's location indicated.

SELF-PORTRAIT OF THE SENDER
The last image shows an outline of the radio telescope at Arecibo, with a sketch of how the radio waves were beamed.

A suspended platform houses transmitters and receivers at the telescope's focus.

EARTH STATION
At 305 metres (1,000 feet) across, the Arecibo radio telescope is the biggest in the world – a bowl of fine wire mesh spanning a natural limestone hollow in Puerto Rico. It spends most of the time "listening in" rather than beaming out, investigating natural sources of radio waves, such as gas clouds, pulsars, and distant galaxies.

Voyaging to the stars
The two starward-bound *Voyager* spacecraft, which flew past Jupiter and Saturn between 1979 and 1981, also carry a message. It's an old-fashioned LP record, complete with a stylus to enable the aliens to play it!

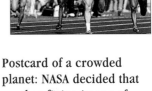

THE SOUNDS OF EARTH
The *Voyager* disc is encoded with sounds and pictures that aim to encapsulate life on Earth. There are greetings in 56 languages (including whale-speak); sounds from a frog-croak to thunder; 90 minutes of music ranging from tribal chants to a Beethoven string quartet; and 118 coded pictures. It will be another 40,000 years before the *Voyagers* speed past their first nearby stars – but the record should last a billion years.

The LP record is made of copper, but gold-plated for protection.

When decoded, one image shows the 200 metres final at the 1972 Munich Olympics. Will the aliens realize this symbolizes the human competitive spirit?

Postcard of a crowded planet: NASA decided that another fitting image of Earth was a packed street scene taken in Lahore, Pakistan.

Talk to the animals
Humans share the Earth with at least two other intelligent species: primates (apes and monkeys) and cetaceans (dolphins and porpoises). Communicating with these species is good practice for speaking alien: but how easy is it?

Dolphins can use a variety of sounds to "name" different objects.

ALIENS ON EARTH
Chimps and dolphins can follow instructions such as "put red brick on top of green" and "swim through hoop". Dolphins can apply a word like "through" to a new situation – for example, "swim through pipe" – and chimps can produce sentences to ask for a banana. These species can use our language, but there is little evidence that they *understand* it. And we do not comprehend the language they use.

Chimps can communicate with humans using signs.

The search begins

THE EMERGING SCIENCE of radio astronomy in the 1950s saw the start of the search for extraterrestrial intelligence (SETI). Scientists speculated that aliens could use radio waves for interstellar communication, just as we use them to transmit radio and TV programmes on Earth. Unlike expensive and energy-hungry spacecraft, radio waves are cheap, can zap across huge gulfs of space at the speed of light, and can be targeted exactly where needed.

COMMUNICATING WITH FIRE, MIRRORS, AND FORESTS

Attempting to contact aliens is not a new idea. In the 19th century, a number of well-respected scientific figures came up with schemes to advertise our existence that seem bizarre today. One advocated digging huge geometrically shaped trenches in the Sahara desert, filling them with oil, and setting fire to them. Another suggested erecting a network of mirrors across Europe in the shape of the stars of the Plough, and using them to beam sunlight to Mars. In 1820, the German mathematician Karl Gauss proposed cutting Siberian forests to form square-shaped stands of trees surrounding a huge triangle to demonstrate Pythagoras' theorem. For want of money, none of the schemes came into operation.

Huge, square-shaped forests surrounding a triangle would tell aliens that there was intelligent life on Earth.

In the 1950s, when a young American, Frank Drake, was working in the brand new field of radio astronomy, aliens were something no respectable scientist thought about. But Drake took a much broader view. Radio dishes, he knew, could pick up naturally produced signals from halfway across the Universe. They could also be used, in reverse, to transmit a signal. He wondered if there were other intelligences out there using telescopes to transmit messages which his instruments should be able to pick up.

Frank Drake devised the "Drake equation" – a formula to calculate how many civilizations might be broadcasting radio signals (pages 102–105).

A cyclopean endeavour

By the early 1970s, astronomer Frank Drake had attracted an enthusiastic band of SETI researchers around him. They began to devise ingenious schemes to eavesdrop on aliens – the most grandiose of which was Project Cyclops (named after the Greek giant with one eye). The "eye" would have consisted of 1,500 huge radio telescopes crowded onto a circular site. But with a price tag equivalent to $50 billion in today's money, it never got off the drawing board.

Project Cyclops would have involved an array of 1,500 radio telescopes packed in a circle of 16 km (10 miles) in diameter, scanning the skies for signals from extraterrestrial sources.

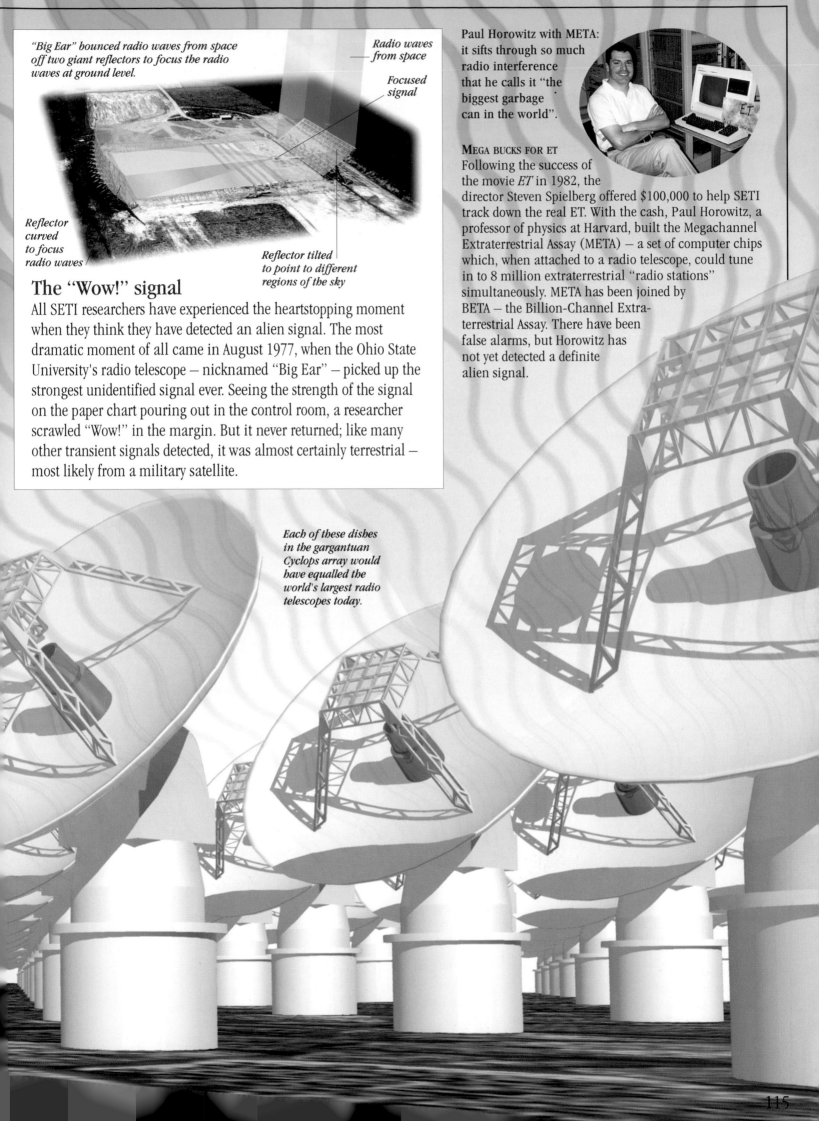

"Big Ear" bounced radio waves from space off two giant reflectors to focus the radio waves at ground level.

Radio waves from space

Focused signal

Reflector curved to focus radio waves

Reflector tilted to point to different regions of the sky

The "Wow!" signal

All SETI researchers have experienced the heartstopping moment when they think they have detected an alien signal. The most dramatic moment of all came in August 1977, when the Ohio State University's radio telescope – nicknamed "Big Ear" – picked up the strongest unidentified signal ever. Seeing the strength of the signal on the paper chart pouring out in the control room, a researcher scrawled "Wow!" in the margin. But it never returned; like many other transient signals detected, it was almost certainly terrestrial – most likely from a military satellite.

Paul Horowitz with META: it sifts through so much radio interference that he calls it "the biggest garbage can in the world".

MEGA BUCKS FOR ET

Following the success of the movie *ET* in 1982, the director Steven Spielberg offered $100,000 to help SETI track down the real ET. With the cash, Paul Horowitz, a professor of physics at Harvard, built the Megachannel Extraterrestrial Assay (META) – a set of computer chips which, when attached to a radio telescope, could tune in to 8 million extraterrestrial "radio stations" simultaneously. META has been joined by BETA – the Billion-Channel Extra-terrestrial Assay. There have been false alarms, but Horowitz has not yet detected a definite alien signal.

Each of these dishes in the gargantuan Cyclops array would have equalled the world's largest radio telescopes today.

ET: please phone Earth!

TODAY, THE SEARCH FOR EXTRATERRESTRIAL INTELLIGENCE (SETI) is considered by most scientists to be a respectable area of research. However, as recently as 1993, US Senators cancelled a $100 million SETI project funded by NASA, deriding it as a "great Martian chase". But now the researchers are back in action with Project Phoenix. Every minute of every day, someone somewhere on Earth is searching for signs of alien intelligence.

OAK RIDGE
A few miles outside Boston, Paul Horowitz (p 115) uses this 26-m (85-ft) telescope for his BETA and META projects. It was first used by Frank Drake.

GOLDSTONE
This dish, in the Mojave Desert in California, was used in NASA's cancelled SETI programme to scan the whole sky.

We've got you covered

SETI has gone worldwide. The map shows locations where searches have been carried out, although not all are still active. SETI researchers now use all kinds of instruments.

 RADIO TELESCOPE
Radio telescopes are still the most efficient SETI tools, because radio waves – which travel almost unimpeded through space – provide an ideal way to communicate.

OPTICAL TELESCOPE
Optical telescopes (and other detectors of shorter wavelength radiation, such as ultraviolet and infrared) are used in searches for unusual signals or alien structures.

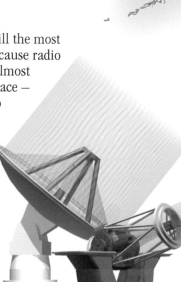

HAT CREEK
California

LEUSCHNER
California

MOUNT WILSON
California

MOUNT LEMMON
Arizona

VERY LARGE ARRAY
New Mexico

ALGONQUIN
Ontario

HAYSTACK
Massachusetts

FIVE COLLEGE
Massachusetts

GREENBANK
West Virginia

COLUMBUS
Ohio

ARECIBO
Puerto Rico

NORTH AMERICA

SOUTH AMERICA

IRAS SATELLITE
In 1983, this satellite detected half a million new "lukewarm" objects in the Universe. Astronomers checked but found no artificial structures.

JILL TARTER
Jill Tarter, of the SETI Institute in California, is probably the most experienced SETI researcher in the world. She followed her degree in engineering physics with research into astrophysics, before combining her two areas of expertise to devise SETI programmes. She currently runs Project Phoenix.

KENT CULLERS
Kent Cullers, also of the SETI Institute, is a computer genius. Although blind since birth, he devises the pattern recognition software that will enable researchers to detect an alien signal in a sea of radio noise.

PARQUE PEREYRA IRAOLA
Argentinean astronomers run BETA and META programmes on this radio telescope near Buenos Aires.

JODRELL BANK
Britain's 76-m (250-ft) telescope has been used for a mobile SETI project by Paul Horowitz, and may become a site for Project Phoenix's "murph" (see below).

COPERNICUS
This satellite — designed to look for natural ultraviolet radiation from objects in space — was also used to seek out artificial laser signals.

ZELENCHUKSKAYA
Astronomers use this 6-m (20-ft) Russian telescope to search for laser signals.

DIY SETI
You don't need to be a scientist to do SETI. The 500 members of the "SETI League" are amateurs who have their own radio dishes. Another way to get involved is to help process the radio signals. An ingenious new project called seti@home feeds part of the signal from the giant Arecibo radio telescope to thousands of home computers. When the computer is idle, a program analyses the data and sends the results back to SETI researchers.

While the SETI program is running, it displays a "screensaver" which shows the region of sky being analysed — here Orion — and then any interesting results.

WESTERBORK
Netherlands

MURMANSK
Russia

EFFELSBERG
Germany

GORKY
Russia

NANÇAY
France

CAUCASUS
Russia

KAMCHATKA
Russia

PAMIR
Tajikistan

MEDICINA
Italy

DEEP SPACE STATION
Ukraine

MARS 2
This Russian probe, which was sent into orbit around the Red Planet in 1972, also carried a detector able to pick up pulsed, artificial radio signals.

PROJECT PHOENIX — RISING AGAIN
Researchers lobbied NASA for 30 years to get funding for a SETI programme. They were devastated when Senators forced NASA to abandon the 10-year project after only one year. Undaunted, the researchers regrouped into a highly visible lobby and began a campaign to attract private funding. Several million dollars poured in — enough to keep the project and personnel afloat for many years to come. Project Phoenix is now managed by Jill Tarter of the SETI Institute.

Project Phoenix's Mobile Research Facility ("murph") can be flown to interface with any radio telescope in the world.

The "murph" is a container van bristling with electronic detection equipment. It can tune in to 28 million frequencies at once.

PERTH
Western Australia

TIDBINBILLA
Australian
Capital Territory

PARKES
In 1995, the 64-m (210-ft) radio telescope in New South Wales became the first destination in the southern hemisphere for Project Phoenix's "murph". Although no alien signals were detected, the team improved the sensitivity of their equipment dramatically.

Cosmic communications

I N 40 YEARS OF LISTENING IN, we have still not heard from ET. Is he the strong and silent type? Or are our methods of communication desperately antiquated? The longer we wait to hear, the more determined the SETI researchers will be to explore all possible ways of picking up that elusive signal. The ultimate SETI facility, bristling with all possible means of cosmic eavesdropping, may not be on Planet Earth at all…

The SETI moonbase

As far as radio signals are concerned, time is running out. Increasing electromagnetic noise on Earth – with equipment ranging from mobile phones to microwave ovens – is fast drowning out the weak whisper from ET. Some SETI researchers are planning to take their search to the far side of the Moon, which is shielded from the interference from Earth. They are seeking protected status for the 100-km (60-mile) diameter Saha crater, where they could build a dedicated SETI facility.

Way beyond us

When the Earth's first radio stations were set up, some people were still communicating with drums or smoke signals, completely oblivious to the radio waves that pass through them. Are we just as unaware of the alien chatter that surrounds us? After all, the Sun and planets are less than half the age of the Universe – so there's every chance that ET will be much more advanced than we are.

The Earth emits ever-increasing electrical noise which leaks away into space. Even a SETI satellite would be swamped with interference.

In orbiting Earth, one side of the Moon – the "far side" – always faces away from us.

The crater Saha, on the far side of the Moon, has a view of space (the yellow zone) that always excludes Earth as the Moon sweeps round its orbit.

Saha, almost on the lunar equator, is only just "around the corner" as seen from Earth. This would allow ships to reach the site more easily.

Lunar SETI Institute and living quarters

The future SETI site contains a radio telescope like Arecibo – but in the weak lunar gravity, it can be even bigger.

Darwin shows the way

To home in on communicating aliens, SETI scientists are looking for other telltale signs of planets with life. *Darwin*, a European space telescope due to be launched in 2015, is designed to seek out life on planets surrounding 300 nearby Sun-like stars. Within this, our local region of space, infrared detectors on *Darwin* will search for signs of water and even oxygen (a by-product of life) on planets as small as Earth.

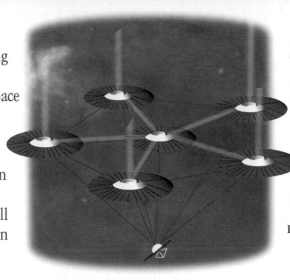

Darwin will comprise six mirrors 50 m (165 ft) apart – equivalent to a telescope 100 m (330 ft) across.

Positioned between Mars and Jupiter, Darwin *will lie beyond the dusty inner Solar System.*

LIGHT YEARS AHEAD

Trying to predict how aliens millions of years ahead of us might communicate is almost impossible. They may signal to one another with laser beams, within reach of our own technology. But they could use even more exotic modes of communication, such as sending streams of tiny subatomic particles called neutrinos which penetrate through clouds in space, stars, and planets alike. Or they could manipulate great masses to create gravitational waves that spread, like ripples, across millions of light years of space. Perhaps they communicate by means that we don't even begin to suspect.

Crystalline cylinders lie at the heart of a "neutrino telescope". Neutrinos may provide intergalactic links on the cosmic internet.

Powerful laser beams shoot into the sky from the Starfire Optical Range in New Mexico: will they carry future interstellar messages?

Large telescopes around the crater seek out laser beam signals and infrared (heat) emissions from large, artificial structures in space.

Tall mast sends messages home via Earth-orbiting satellites.

Solar panels strung out along the crater rim collect energy to provide power for the base.

A neutrino telescope, buried to avoid contamination from other radiations, searches for signals from advanced aliens.

Laser beams travelling along the surface of the crater should register gravitational waves created by aliens manipulating massive bodies such as black holes.

Galactic civilizations

Z
Y
X
W
V
U
T
S

THE FIRST ALIEN MESSAGE we decipher is likely to come from a civilization more advanced than our own. Humans, after all, are the new kids on the cosmic block. Many stars are far older than the Sun, and could have civilizations way ahead of us. It is impossible to know what intelligent lifeforms might look like after billions more years of evolution. But scientists predict they will follow similar paths in exploiting energy and information, building vast structures, and perhaps setting up an intergalactic network of communications.

Dyson Sphere

If SETI researchers find a large star giving out lots of infrared heat but little light, they may have located a Dyson Sphere. Made from dismantled planets, the sphere surrounds the star to trap all its energy. Civilizations live on the inside surface of the sphere, with the star always overhead providing a clean, limitless source of power.

R

Information vs energy

Q
P
O
N
M
L
K

Far-sighted scientists have suggested a scheme for comparing how far alien civilizations have advanced, regardless of how they may look or the nature of their culture. One measure of their progress is controlling energy; another is manipulating information. The graph on this page plots increasing exploitation of energy (left to right, from 0 to 4.4) and processing of information (up the page, from A to Z). Each coloured box represents a different combination of information and energy that a civilization could control. We can show Earth's progress to date so far (the solid line), and we would expect our future progress, and that of civilizations ahead of us, to continue on a diagonal path (dashed) of increasing energy and information manipulation.

Blow-up of cross section through the sphere.

At 1.4 J, a civilization has sufficient energy and information processing to establish regular communications with alien cultures.

At 2.2 L, a civilization can alter its parent star to act as an interstellar beacon.

J
I

Our civilization moved sideways (from 0.1 to 0.6) after harnessing the energy of coal, oil, and nuclear power (the Industrial Revolution), then upwards (E to H) after it learnt to manipulate information with computers (the Information Revolution).

H
G
F
E
D
C
B
A

Information manipulation

Industrial Revolution

Information Revolution

At 0.6 H, Earth is only just on the energy-information graph.

FREEMAN J. DYSON

In 1960, British physicist Freeman Dyson (b. 1923) suggested advanced civilizations might surround their stars with artificial habitats — "Dyson Spheres" — to exploit energy to the maximum. Dramatically ahead of his time, he also proposed that humans could genetically modify our bodies to adapt to living in space. Although astronomers have searched for the infrared "heat-energy" signals from Dyson Spheres, none has been found.

Dyson's conventional work spans nuclear and particle physics.

CLASSIFYING CIVILIZATIONS

The idea of ranking civilizations by energy use was devised by Russian scientist Nicolai Kardashev in 1964. A decade later, American astronomer Carl Sagan suggested grading them by their ability to process information as well.

Type I civilization

Can harness the entire energy of its planet.

Energy manipulation →

| 0 | 0.2 | 0.4 | 0.6 | 0.8 | 1.0 | 1.2 | 1.4 | 1.6 | 1.8 | 2.0 |

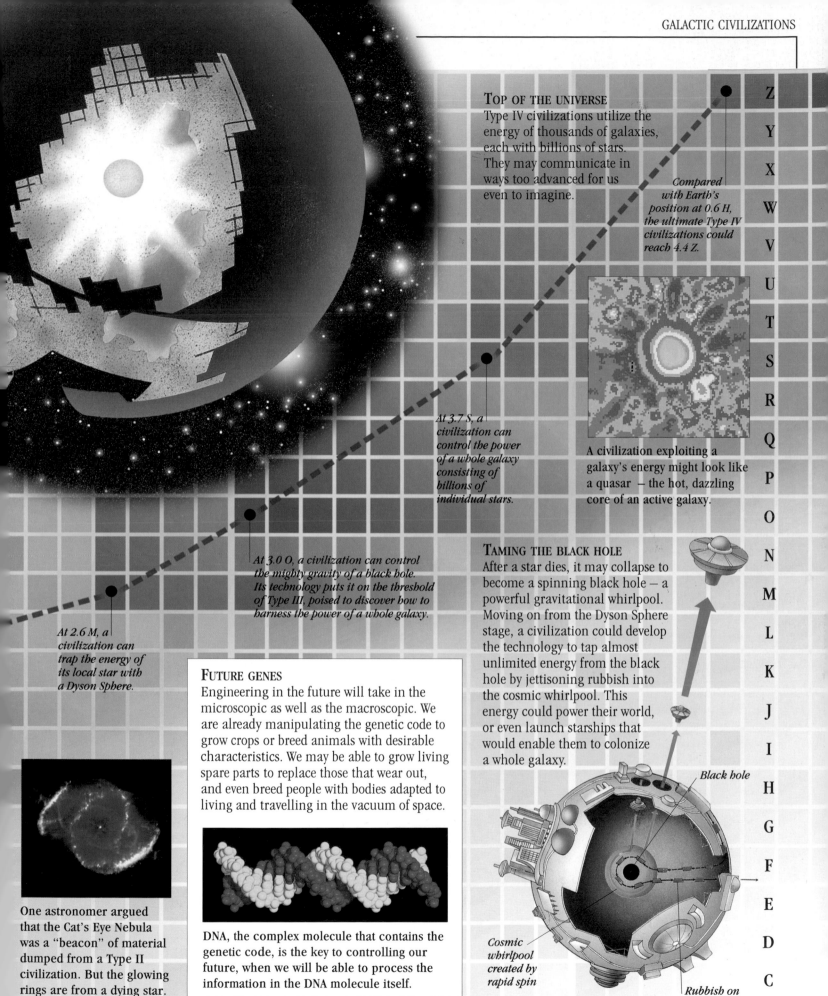

TOP OF THE UNIVERSE
Type IV civilizations utilize the energy of thousands of galaxies, each with billions of stars. They may communicate in ways too advanced for us even to imagine.

Compared with Earth's position at 0.6 H, the ultimate Type IV civilizations could reach 4.4 Z.

At 3.7 S, a civilization can control the power of a whole galaxy consisting of billions of individual stars.

A civilization exploiting a galaxy's energy might look like a quasar — the hot, dazzling core of an active galaxy.

At 3.0 O, a civilization can control the mighty gravity of a black hole. Its technology puts it on the threshold of Type III, poised to discover how to harness the power of a whole galaxy.

TAMING THE BLACK HOLE
After a star dies, it may collapse to become a spinning black hole — a powerful gravitational whirlpool. Moving on from the Dyson Sphere stage, a civilization could develop the technology to tap almost unlimited energy from the black hole by jettisoning rubbish into the cosmic whirlpool. This energy could power their world, or even launch starships that would enable them to colonize a whole galaxy.

At 2.6 M, a civilization can trap the energy of its local star with a Dyson Sphere.

FUTURE GENES
Engineering in the future will take in the microscopic as well as the macroscopic. We are already manipulating the genetic code to grow crops or breed animals with desirable characteristics. We may be able to grow living spare parts to replace those that wear out, and even breed people with bodies adapted to living and travelling in the vacuum of space.

Black hole

One astronomer argued that the Cat's Eye Nebula was a "beacon" of material dumped from a Type II civilization. But the glowing rings are from a dying star.

DNA, the complex molecule that contains the genetic code, is the key to controlling our future, when we will be able to process the information in the DNA molecule itself.

Cosmic whirlpool created by rapid spin

Rubbish on conveyor belt

| Z | Y | X | W | V | U | T | S | R | Q | P | O | N | M | L | K | J | I | H | G | F | E | D | C | B | A |

Type II civilization
Exploits the energy of its star.

Type III civilization
Utilizes the complete energy of its home galaxy.

Type IV civilization
Controls a cluster of galaxies.

| 2.4 | 2.6 | 2.8 | 3.0 | 3.2 | 3.4 | 3.6 | 3.8 | 4.0 | 4.2 | 4.4 |

Ultimate aliens

IN OUR QUEST FOR SIGNS OF ALIEN INTELLIGENCE in the Universe, we may have missed a trick. Perhaps other lifeforms might not resemble us in any way, so they also think and behave in ways that are very different. There may even be lifeforms out there so extreme or so unexpected that we wouldn't recognize them as living. But what do we mean by "living": how do you define what life is? And when it comes to "intelligence", we encounter the same problem – perhaps some aliens reason so differently from us that communication with them would be an impossibility.

Most spiral galaxies spin much more quickly than expected.

The dark matter in and around a galaxy provides a gravitational pull that keeps the spinning galaxy together.

Spot the alien

We can only guess some of the ways in which alien life could be totally unlike ours. Every image on this page is a kind of "life" that has been proposed at some time by a distinguished scientist. Some may involve different chemistry, adapted to extreme environments. Others may be formless and diffuse, or comprise all the lifeforms on one planet as a single huge entity. A few scientists maintain that the Universe itself is alive. Weirdest of all, some aliens may be forever invisible to us, yet passing silently through our bodies every second of the day.

GAIA
The Gaia hypothesis, named after the Greek Earth goddess, maintains that a whole planet can be a living entity. Its plants, animals, atmosphere, and ocean act together to preserve a long-term balance. Any individual species upsetting that balance – such as human beings – risks being destroyed.

SILICON LIFEFORMS
The element silicon combines with other elements in a similar way to carbon, so some scientists have speculated that it could form life. The crystalline silicon-based life on this airless asteroid organizes itself into an intelligent society like a collection of silicon microchips, and can thrive in the vacuum of space and lethal radiation.

The meaning of life
Even scientists cannot agree how to define what life really is. Some say that a living entity uses energy in an orderly way, has a boundary, and can reproduce. Even on Earth, however, that definition isn't watertight, as shown below. When it comes to truly alien environments, perhaps there is no clear distinction between life and non-life.

If a "living entity" has a "boundary, uses energy, and reproduces", then a flame is alive.

If reproduction is essential to life, then the mule – a sterile cross between an ass and a horse – is not alive.

IS THE UNIVERSE ALIVE?

A controversial new theory states that a whole universe can be alive, judged by the idea that life involves success in reproduction. The theory holds that black holes can "bud" whole universes. Those which develop black holes are successful; those that do not are sterile. By a strange quirk of physics, a universe that forms black holes also makes the right chemicals for life like us.

INVISIBLE LIFE?

Studies of spinning galaxies reveal that they are much more massive than at first appears. The extra mass – known as "dark matter" – is invisible and its nature is unknown. Dark matter permeates the whole of the Milky Way and other galaxies, and extends into a large halo that surrounds individual galaxies. If dark matter could build lifeforms, they would be invisible and even capable of passing through our bodies without us being aware of them.

Astronomers believe that more than 90% of the Universe consists of invisible, dark matter.

Interstellar clouds are black because they contain dust – "soot" from dying stars. Lit by intense light from a star, the black cloud glows a dull brown.

A black hole in our Universe "buds" a baby universe. This expands and, if it contains black holes, can itself reproduce.

BLACK CLOUDS

Stars are born in dense black clouds of dust and molecules of gas, such as ammonia and carbon dioxide, that emit microwave radiation. In his novel *The Black Cloud*, the astronomer Fred Hoyle imagined that a cloud like this could be intelligent, with molecules communicating by microwaves like nerve cells in a brain. But the cloud needs energy to stay "alive", which means feeding on light from a nearby star – in this case, the Sun. In the book, the repercussions for Earth are not very pleasant.

The Milky Way contains over 5,000 dense dark clouds, each potentially a "Black Cloud" alien.

Starship designer

Bob Forward, who invented "cheelas", is a science fiction writer and was formerly an aerospace engineer with the Hughes Aircraft Corporation. He has designed futuristic spaceships which, if built, could travel to the stars at velocities approaching the speed of light. The spaceships would be vast wire-mesh sails, the size of Texas, propelled along by immensely powerful lasers that stay in orbit around the Sun.

Bob Forward's imaginative designs extend to his famous waistcoats, such as this rainbow one.

CHEELAS

Apart from black holes, neutron stars have the strongest gravity of any object in the Universe. Space engineer Bob Forward has suggested flattened beings made of the nuclei of atoms – "cheelas" – could live on their searingly hot surfaces. Their life processes depend not on chemistry but on nuclear reactions.

Living on the incandescent surface of a neutron star, cheelas see everything lit from below.

First contact

THE DAY WE DETECT A SIGNAL from extraterrestrial intelligence will be a turning point in the history of the world. We will know, at last, that we are not alone. The shock waves of the discovery will be felt far beyond the community of SETI scientists. The signal will have an impact on everybody, from heads of government and the world's religious communities through to ordinary individuals – and every group will react in a different way. In the end, there will be two decisions to be made. Should we respond? And, if so, what should we say?

Detection!

Events begin to unfold in 2020 with the detection of an obviously alien signal by Project Phoenix researchers at Greenbank, West Virginia. The signal – called a "carrier wave" – reveals the frequency of the alien broadcast, but it is too weak for any information to be decoded.

CARL SAGAN
Carl Sagan (1934–1996) was one of the most influential proponents of SETI. He was equally comfortable in the fields of astronomy and biology, working on Martian life experiments on the *Viking* missions before becoming a staunch and visionary advocate of SETI. He devised our first messages to the stars sent aboard the *Pioneer* and *Voyager* spacecraft.

Sagan's novel *Contact* gave an illuminating perspective on our reaction to alien signals.

Unidentified signal coming from the constellation Piscis Austrinus, which is picked up by the Greenbank radio telescope

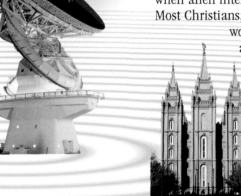

Project Phoenix radio telescope at Greenbank

PROTOCOL
The SETI researchers follow the "Declaration of Principles for Activities Following the Detection of Extraterrestrial Intelligence" – guidelines accepted internationally in 1990.

RELIGIOUS RESPONSE
Religions may be thrown into turmoil when alien intelligence is detected. Most Christians, for example, would worry whether Jesus had also lived and died on these other planets. The Mormon doctrine, though, includes a strong belief in other inhabited worlds.

The Mormon Church is not surprised by the alien signal.

POLITICAL RESPONSE
At the White House, the US President confirms her commitment to SETI. In order to decode the signal, a huge, very sensitive array of radio telescopes must be built. She promises to fund it – just as President Clinton committed more money to Mars research after a possible Martian microfossil was found in 1996.

VERIFICATION
One of the protocols in the Declaration of Principles is that the signal must be verified by other teams before it is announced. Several groups of radio astronomers around the world successfully detect the carrier wave. But still no message emerges from the weak signal.

TELLING THE WORLD
The discoverers, having told the relevant professional bodies and the Secretary-General of the United Nations, go public at a press conference. There can be no cover-up: SETI researchers believe in openness.

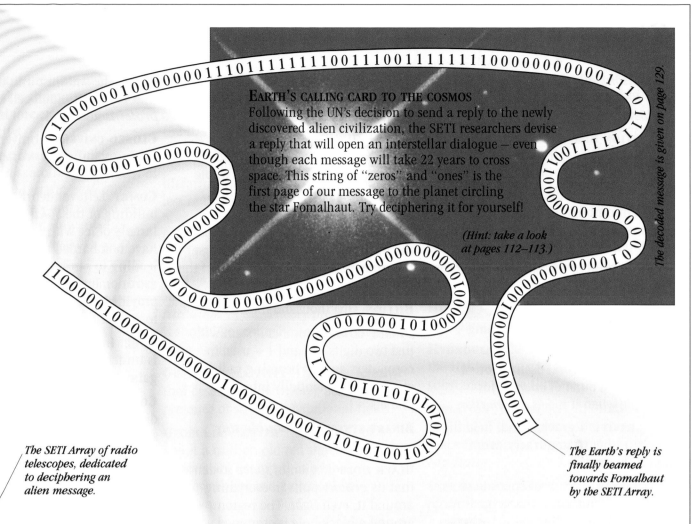

1000000011101111111100111001111111110000000000001110111111001111111110000001000000

EARTH'S CALLING CARD TO THE COSMOS
Following the UN's decision to send a reply to the newly discovered alien civilization, the SETI researchers devise a reply that will open an interstellar dialogue — even though each message will take 22 years to cross space. This string of "zeros" and "ones" is the first page of our message to the planet circling the star Fomalhaut. Try deciphering it for yourself!

(Hint: take a look at pages 112–113.)

The decoded message is given on page 129.

The SETI Array of radio telescopes, dedicated to deciphering an alien message.

The Earth's reply is finally beamed towards Fomalhaut by the SETI Array.

PUBLIC RESPONSE
The public reacts in a bewildering variety of ways to the news. Some people are euphoric; others feel threatened. The press, at first serious, soon starts to feature alien cartoons, while television cannot show enough old sci-fi movies. Stock markets oscillate wildly as nervous people speculate. A few of the more extreme religious sects commit mass suicide. The military grows cautious. But everyone has been changed, knowing that we have company out there in space.

Stock exchanges react nervously to news of the extraterrestrial signal.

The strangest and most important United Nations debate of all: should we reply to an alien message?

SETI research suddenly becomes a vote winner.

WHAT DOES THE MESSAGE CONTAIN?
Three years later, the powerful SETI Array of radio telescopes is complete. It easily captures the carrier wave, and is powerful enough to reveal within this signal a wealth of complex detail. This is the longed-for message. Experts work on it for months, but only partly succeed in decoding it. The message tells of the language and science of the inhabitants of a planet around the star Fomalhaut, 22 light years away. But there is much that is indecipherable, to await researchers of the future.

SHOULD WE REPLY?
Now the United Nations is charged with a huge responsibility: should it reply on behalf of the people of Earth? Some experts speak passionately against, arguing that if "they" are hostile, they are close enough on the cosmic scale to travel to Earth and destroy us. But the SETI community convinces the UN that the benefits of contact will outweigh the risks — and are asked to draft a response.

Useful Addresses

Clubs and Societies

Virtually every town in the UK has a locally based astronomical society – check at your library

British Astronomical Association, Burlington House, Piccadilly, London W1V 9AG (The UK's society for active amateur astronomers)

Society for Popular Astronomy, c/o Guy Fennimore, 36 Fairway, Keyworth, Notts NG12 5DU (Society for beginners and "armchair astronomers")

Observatories, Planetariums, and Visitor Attractions

Armagh Observatory and Planetarium, College Hill, Armagh, Northern Ireland BT61 9DB

Central Museum and Planetarium, Victoria Avenue, Southend-on-Sea, Essex SS2 6EW

City Observatory, Calton Hill, Edinburgh, Lothian EH7 5AA

Glasgow College of Nautical Studies Planetarium, 21 Thistle Street, Glasgow G5 9XB

Herschel House and Museum, 19 New King Street, Bath, Avon BA1 2BL

Herstmonceux Science Centre, Herstmonceux Castle, nr Hailsham, East Sussex BN27 1RP

Jeremiah Horrocks Observatory, Moor Park, Preston, Lancs PR1 6AD

Jewel and Esk Valley College Planetarium, 24 Milton Road East, Edinburgh, Lothian EH15 2PP

Jodrell Bank Science Centre and Planetarium, Lower Withington, Macclesfield, Cheshire SK11 9DL

Liverpool Museum Planetarium, William Brown Street, Liverpool, Merseyside L3 8EN

London Planetarium, Marylebone Road, London NW1 5LR

Mills Observatory, Balgay Park, Dundee, Tayside DD2 2UB

National Space Science Centre, Leicester (Due to open in 2000)

Norman Lockyer Observatory, Salcombe Hill, Sidmouth, Devon EX10 0NY

Old Royal Observatory and Greenwich Planetarium, National Maritime Museum, Romney Road, Greenwich, London SE10 9NF

Plymouth Planetarium, School of Maritime Studies, Plymouth, Devon PL4 8AA

Royal Observatory Edinburgh, Blackford Hill, Edinburgh, Lothian EH9 3HJ

South Tyneside College Planetarium and Observatory, St George's Avenue, South Shields, Tyne and Wear NE34 6ET

University of London Observatory, Department of Physics & Astronomy, 553 Watford Way, London NW7 2QS

University Observatory, St Andrews, Department of Physics & Astronomy, University of St Andrews, St Andrews, Fife KY16 9SS

Acknowledgements

The publisher would like to thank the following for their kind permission to reproduce their photographs:

a=above; b=below; c=centre; l=left; r=right; t=top

American Institute of Physics: Emilio Segre Visual Archives, Physics Today Collection 24br; Dorothy Davis Locanthu 34bl; **Ancient Art & Architecture Collection**: 33cr; **Bridgeman Art Library**: Bible Society 32cl; Louvre 32b; **California Institute of Technology**: 56br; Bob Paz 83tr; **Camera Press**: 124bc, 125br; Erma 79tl; John Reader, ILN 30bc; **Bruce Coleman Ltd**: 113bra, 113bc; **Colorific**: Steve Smith 124tr; **Corbis UK**: 107tc, 119cl; **Mary Evans Picture Library**: 33tl, 40cl, 90tr; Explorer 40clb; **Eye Ubiquitous**: Barry Davies 124crb; **"Face on Mars" Home Page**: Internet 98cr; **Fortean Picture Library**: 107cl; **Galaxy Picture Library**: 108tr, 112cl; **Getty Images**: 106bc, 106-107bc; **H. Hammel**: MIT & NASA 95bl; **Hencoup Enterprises**: 79cr, 91tl, 110tr, 114tc, 115tr, 116tr, 117btl, 117bc, 123br; NASA 99bl, 101tc; NASA, SETI Institute 116tc; RAL 116cba; **Images Colour Library**: 106cl, 106cr, 107br; **Image Select**: 62tr; **Instituto Argentino de Radioastronomia**: 116br;

Jodrell Bank: University of Manchester 29br; **Keystone, Zurich**: 108cl; **Kobal Collection**: 90cl, 90bl, 90c, 90bcl, 90bcr, 90brb, 91br, 91cr, 91crb, 91clb, 91clrb, 91bl, 91bca; **Lowell Observatory**: 96tcr, 96cra; **Massachusetts Institute of Technology**: Donna Coveney 18tr; **Max-Planck-Institut Für Quantenoptik**: 85tr; **NASA**: 20cl, 116bcl; **Natural History Museum**: 43bl; **Ohio State University Archives**: 115tl; **Pictor International**: 20br; **Planet Earth Pictures**: Space Frontiers Ltd 2-3; **Faculty Files, Princeton University Archives**: (used with permission Princeton University Library) 65bc; **Rex Features**: 124brb (montage); **Robert Harding Picture Library**: 33br; **Ronald Grant Archive**: 90bra, 91cla, 91cra, 91blr; Castle Premier/Interscope Communications/Soissons-Murphey Productions/De Laurentis Film Partners ("Bill & Ted's Excellent Adventure") 76tr; **Royal Edinburgh Observatory**: Anglo Australian Telescope Board, David Malin 46bl; **San Francisco State University**: 108clb; **Science Photo Library**: 22br, 43br, 92bl, 119cr, 121bl; Dr. C. Alcock, MACHO Collaboration 84br, 85bc; Axel Bartel 125cl; Julian Baum 95cr, 99cr; Californian Association for Research in Astronomy 95bca; CERN 35c; J. L. Charmet 60tr; John Chumack 125tr; Dr. Ray Clark & Marwyn Goff 28tr; T. Craddock 80tr; Dr. Eli, Brinks 37br;

Clive Freman, Royal Institution 19cb; Tony Hallas 19bc; Harvard College Observatory 41cr; Hencoup Enterprises 57tl; A. Howarth 68cl; Lawrence Berkeley Laboratory 78bl; Los Alamos National Laboratory 21br; Cern, P. Loitez 16b; W. & D. McIntyre 69tl; Max-Planck-Institut Für Extraterrestrische Physik 58cl; A. Morton, D. Millon 80cl; NASA 28bl, 56tr, 60bc, 60br, 87ca, 98tc, 98cr, 98cl, 112br, 113trb; Novosti 117tlb; Space Telescope Science Institute 54bl, 82bl, 84bl; NRAO, AUI 52bl, 81cr, 81br, 83bl; NRAO, F. Yusef-Zadeh 81bl; D. Parker 59br; John Reader 92br; Royal Observatory, Edinburgh, ATTB 54tr; Rev. R. Royer 62cl; F. Sauze 66tr; Francoise Sauze 20bc; Dr. Rudolph Schild 41tr; Dr. K. Seddon & Dr. T. Evans, Queen's University Belfast 120cb, 121bc; Dr. Seth Shostak 112br; Smithsonian Institution 57cl; Space Telescope Science Institute, NASA 25br, 31tl, 31cl; Starlight 20c; Starlight, Roger Ressmeyer 27cr; US Geological Survey 96cl, 97tr; X-Ray Astronomy Group, Leicester University 121tr; **SETI Institute**: Dr. Seth Shostack 116bl, 124cla, 124bl; **South American Pictures**: 107cra; **Telegraph Colour Library**: 124bra (montage); **Topham Picturepoint**: 113cra; **United Nations, Wolf**: 113crb; **Universal Pictorial Press & Agency**: 94bl; **Werner Forman Archive**: Liverpool Museum 33tr; **Zefa**: 67br, 69cla.